An [...] to the E[...]pace

SI[...]

First published in Great Britain in 1993 by
Simon & Schuster Education
Campus 400, Maylands Avenue
Hemel Hempstead, Herts HP2 7EZ

Printed in Great Britain by
BPCC Hazell Books
Paulton and Aylesbury

A catalogue record of this book is
available from the British Library

ISBN 0 7501 0235 7

This book considers those parts of the National Curriculum Science Programme that are not covered in the other books in the 'Early Start' series. It is particularly concerned with water, the atmosphere and the structure of the Earth. The variety of life to be found on Earth is outlined. Both the Earth's place in space and other bodies in space are considered.

Like the other books in the series, it introduces children to the processes of:

- *exploration of their environment in order to gather experiences at first hand*
- *manipulation of objects and materials*
- *observation of things around them*
- *questioning and arguing about things*
- *testing things out, performing simple problem solving activities*
- *looking for pattern and relationship.*

Together with the other books in the series:

An Early Start to Science
An Early Start to Nature
An Early Start to Technology from Science
An Early Start to the Environment
An Early Start to Ourselves and Evolution
An Early Start to Energy

it provides comprehensive coverage for teachers of the whole Science National Curriculum up to Key Stage 2. The activities are presented in a highly visual, easily accessible form. They stress the importance of scientific method as embodied in Attainment Target 1, Scientific Investigation, and at the same time give thorough coverage of the scientific knowledge outlined in the other attainment targets. The aim of the series has been to create a succinct, informative, accessible and manageable scheme for National Curriculum Primary Science.

I hope you enjoy the activities in this book.

Roy Richards

Safety in schools

All the activities in this book are safe provided they are properly organised and supervised in accordance with the recommendations of the DES, the Health and Safety Executive, the Association for Science Education, and local authority regulations. Any teachers who are uncertain about safety in scientific and technical work should consult their LEA advisers. They should also read 'Be safe: some aspects of safety in science and technology in primary schools', published by the Association for Science Education.

Always pack away potentially dangerous apparatus and chemicals immediately the activity is over.

Red triangles

Some activities in this book do require extra care and attention. They are marked with a red triangle. Under no circumstances should children be allowed to pursue them unsupervised, particularly during breaks.

For many thousands of years people believed the Earth was flat.

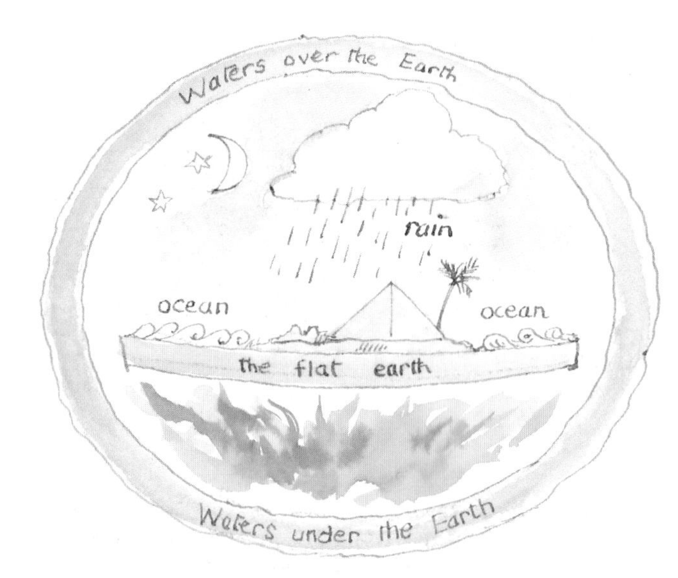

Scientists speak of the Earth as having three main layers:

- *The central core is about 6,000 km wide and made mostly of iron. The outer core is liquid and the inner solid.*
- *It is surrounded by the mantle, which is about 2,900 km thick and is made up of dense, very hot rocks, mostly solid but with some molten material.*
- *The outer layer on which we live is called the crust. Under the oceans it is about 6 km thick but under continents it is between 30 and 60 km thick, the thickest parts being under the mountain chains.*
  The crust holds the oceans, known as the hydrosphere. The crust is surrounded by the atmosphere, which extends upward for thousands of kilometres, though most of the air is in the lower layers – at 60 km air pressure is only a thousandth of that at sea level.

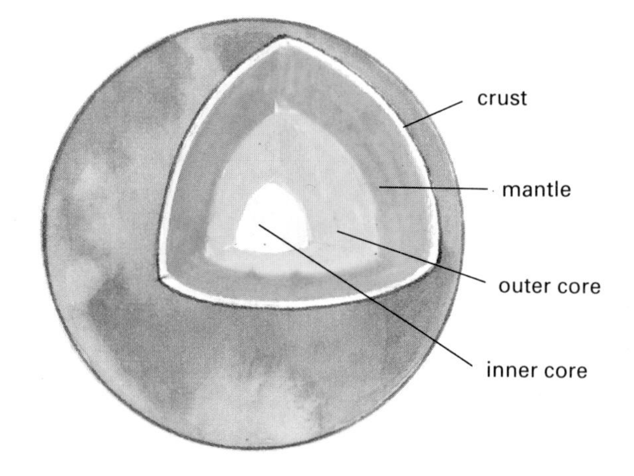

The Earth is slightly wider across the Equator than from pole to pole. Its average diameter is about 12,740 km. The Earth's mass is about 6,000 million, million, million tonnes. Three-fifths of the Earth's surface is water, two-fifths is land.

The Earth is one of nine planets in our solar system. Its size relative to the Sun and the other planets in the system is shown below. Of course, this diagram does not show their relative positions.

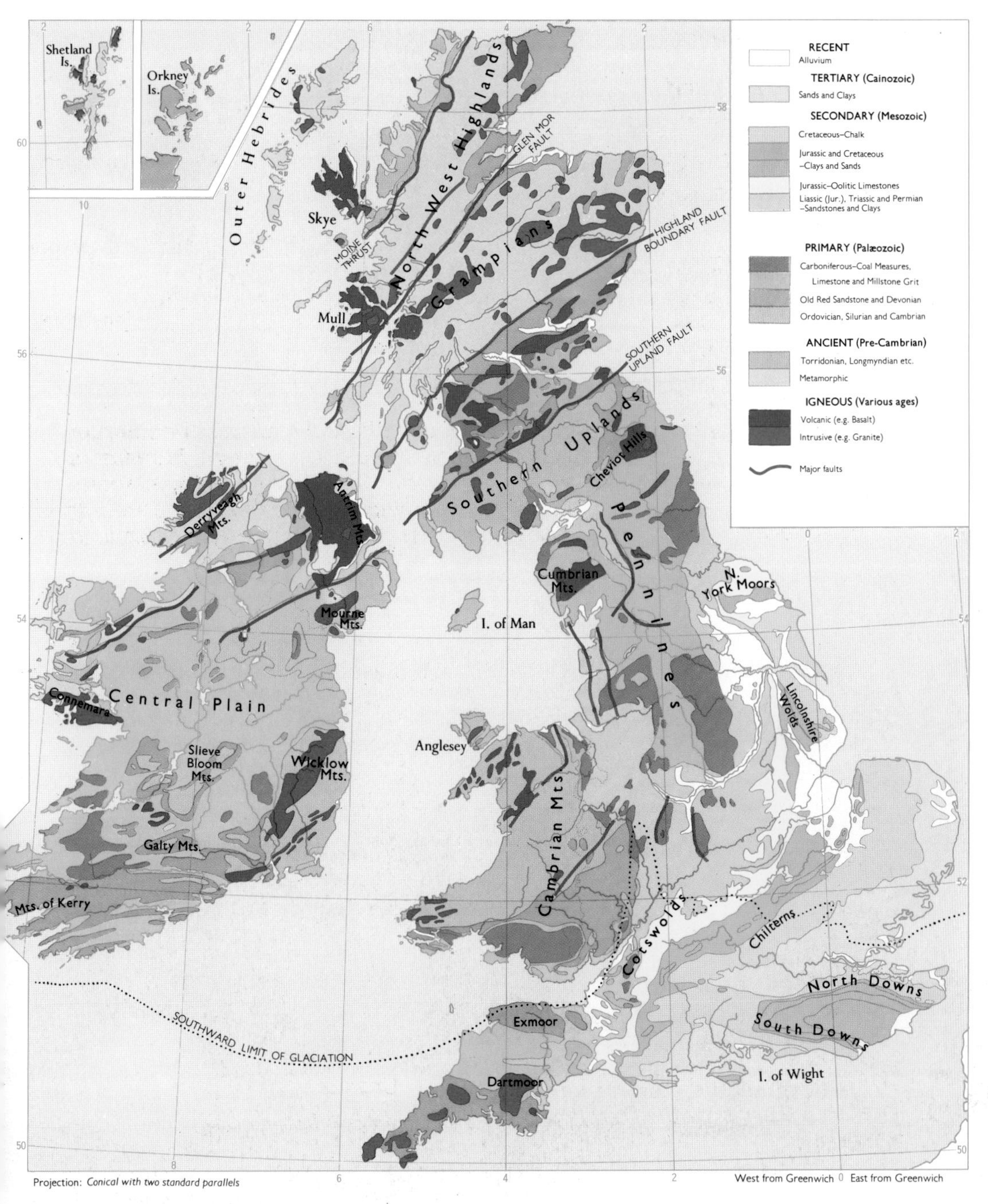

Geological map of the British Isles

There are a number of ways to begin a study of the rocks and soils in the vicinity of the school. A good start is to collect rocks from the immediate area. Such a survey is described in 'An Early Start to the Environment', pages 64-7, where tests to carry out on rocks and pebbles are also described.

With older children a study of the solid geology map of the area is helpful in relating rocks found to the underlying strata. Outcrops of rock and quarries in an area can also be useful for providing specimens. Scientific suppliers are a source of named specimens of rock.

Soil

Soil is formed by the breakdown of rock through weathering and the addition of organic material (decaying plant and animal material).

Sometimes soils bear no relationship to the underlying rock. Such soil has been transported by water, by wind or often by ice sheets in the Ice Age.

See 'An Early Start to Nature', pages 58-9, for further work on soils.

When children examine rocks they will notice that a number are made up of, or contain, crystals of different shapes, sizes and colours. Crystals are not uncommon in a child's world, for salt and sugar and bath salts are found in the home. A start can be made by examining these.

sugar (sucrose)

bath salts (mostly sodium carbonate)

Epsom salts (magnesium sulphate)

health salts (usually sodium bicarbonate and citric acid; they react in water to give sodium citrate)

Salt

Put some hot water into a Pyrex bowl and stir in salt until no more will dissolve.

Pour some of the mixture on to a saucer, taking care not to pour out any undissolved salt. Leave it in a warm place for the water to evaporate.

The slower the evaporation, the bigger the crystals.

You will be left with a crust of cube-shaped crystals. Examine them with a hand lens. Try crushing the crystals – they will break into smaller, cube-shaped crystals.

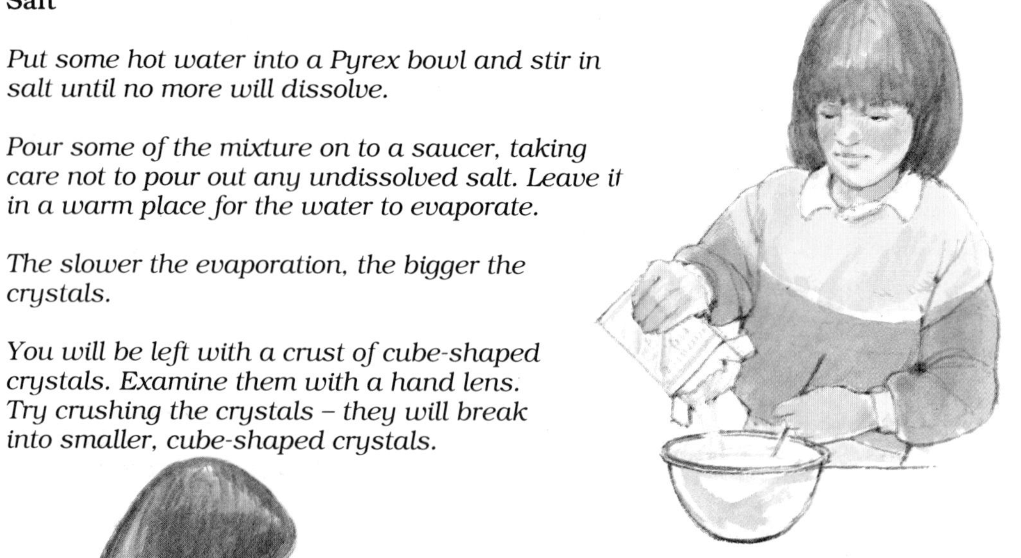

Although it is important to show children that crystals can be obtained in this manner, the results are not impressive. Examining dry salt crystals with a hand lens or binocular microscope will give better definition of crystal shapes.

Try growing other crystals in this way.

Growing larger crystals

Potash alum (aluminium potassium sulphate) will give good sized crystals.

1. *Dissolve as much as possible in a mug of warm water.*
2. *Hang a length of cotton from a pencil so that it dangles into the mixture.*
3. *Leave for a few days. Tiny crystals will start to appear on the thread and in the mug.*
4. *Remove the thread very gently from the mug and suspend it in a clean jam jar.*

5. *Gently fill the jar with potash alum solution. Cover it with a clean piece of cotton cloth to keep the dust out. Leave.*

The crystals grow as the solution becomes more concentrated through evaporation of the water.

Chrome alum and copper sulphate are two other crystals commonly grown.

Make a crystal garden

Crystals can also be set into sodium silicate solution, where they 'grow', giving a pretty effect. Sodium silicate solution is somewhat gelatinous and was formerly used, under the name of 'waterglass', for preserving eggs.

This is best done as a teacher demonstration as some of the chemicals are poisonous.

Begin by diluting the sodium silicate with an equal amount of water. Put it in a large jam jar.

Drop in two or three of each kind of crystal that you want to use.

Crystals that give good effects are:
- *potash alum (aluminium potassium sulphate)*
- *ferric alum (ferric ammonium sulphate)*
- *copper sulphate*
- *nickel sulphate*
- *manganese sulphate*
- *cobalt chloride*

Some crystals grow very rapidly.

Leave the garden overnight. Don't move it. The crystals will 'grow' upward in wavy strands.

set the jar where you want the garden to grow

Crystal shapes

Crystals come in geometric shapes. These are some:

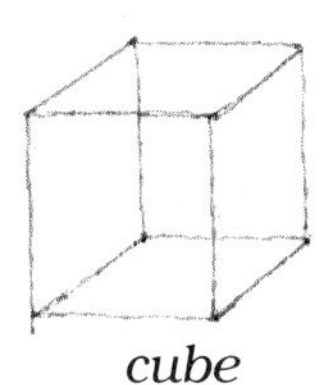
cube

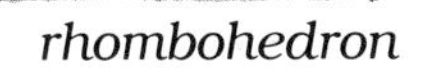
rhombohedron

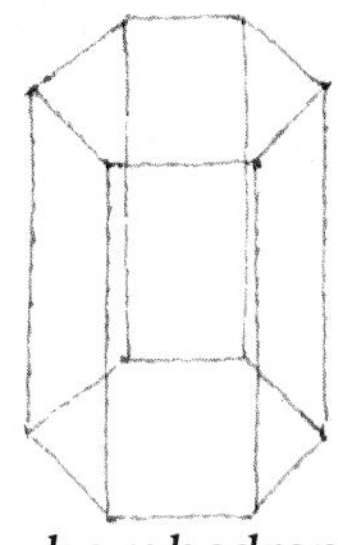
hexahedron

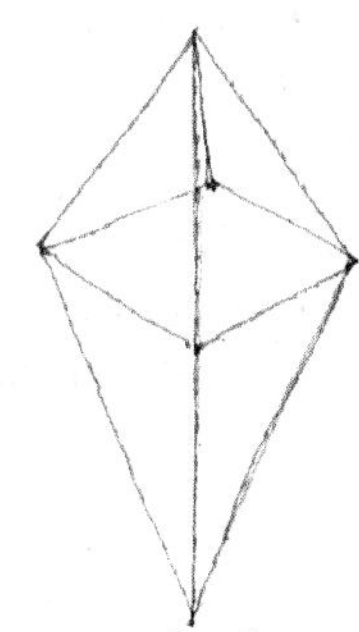
octahedron

Nets for a cube, rhombohedron and hexahedron are easy to construct. Here is one for an octahedron.

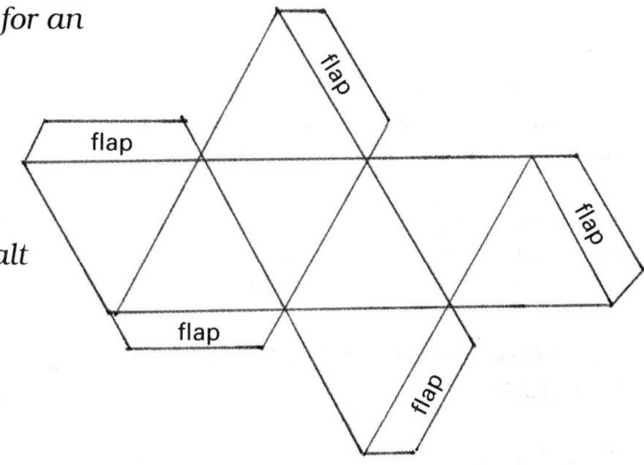

Use nets to make each of these crystals shapes from card.

Samples of fluorite, quartz, rock salt and calcite are available from scientific suppliers. They are all excellent examples of crystals. Match your card models of crystal shapes with the crystals.

Fluorite and rock salt are cubic. Quartz and calcite are hexahedra. Calcite cleaves (splits) into rhombohedra. Fluorite cleaves into octahedra.

fluorite (calcium fluoride)

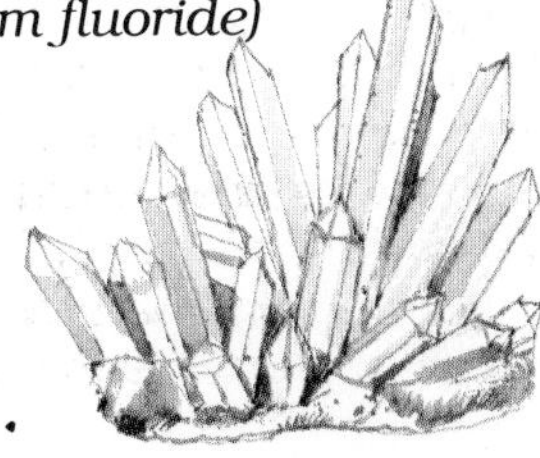
quartz (silicon dioxide)

rock salt (sodium chloride)

calcite (calcium carbonate)

Soil constituents

Soils are composed mostly of fragments of rock.

Use a trowel to dig up soil from the soil surface to a depth of 15 cm. Put it in a plastic bag. Dig soil from a depth of 15 cm to a depth of 30 cm. Put this in a second plastic bag.

Secure each bag with an elastic band, and label it.

Back in school, take some of the soil from one bag and break it up quite finely.

Put this into a clear plastic bottle, almost fill with water, put on the stopper and shake for a few minutes.

Repeat the procedure with the soil from the second sample.

The largest soil particles (gravel) settle first. The finest (clay) settle last.

It is possible to estimate the amount of each in the sample. For example, if the gravel measures one-fifth of the height of the solids in the bottle then it is 20% of the sample.

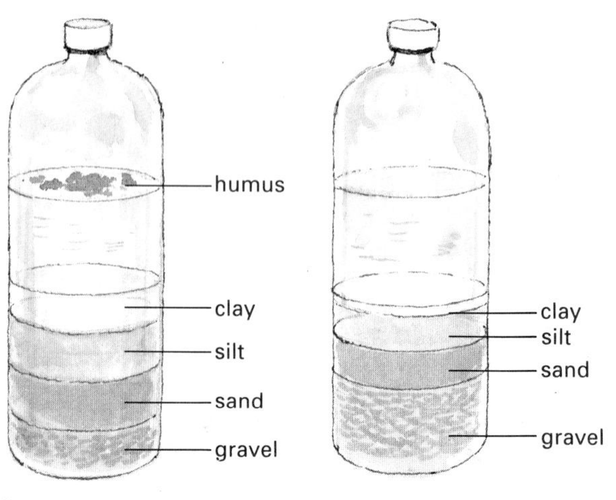

first sample *second sample*

Water content

Again you need to use the two separate samples of soil that have already been collected.

Weigh a tin lid and make a record of its mass.

Put some soil in the tin lid and reweigh. Make a record.

Heat the soil at 100°C over two school days until it is dried. Let the tin lid and soil cool. Reweigh.

Repeat with the second soil sample.

Humus content

Again do this with both soil samples.

The relatively gentle heating in the previous experiment should have driven off the water but not destroyed the humus (decaying plant and animal material.

The soil in each sample from the previous experiment now needs to be cooked in a very hot oven until the humus is burnt off.

Make sure the tin lids are cold before reweighing.

Compare the amount of water and the amount of humus in the top layer of the soil (to 15 cm deep) with that in the next layer (from 15 cm to 30 cm deep).

page 1

How much water is there in the soil?

Mass of tin lid + soil = 30g
Mass of tin lid = 20g
Mass of soil = 10g

Mass of tin lid + soil (after heating) = 28g
Mass of tin lid = 20g
Mass of soil (after heating) = 8g

Amount of water lost = 10g − 8g = 2g

$$\text{Percentage water content} = \frac{\text{mass of water lost} \times 100}{\text{mass of dry soil}}$$

$$= \frac{2}{10} \times 100 = 20\%$$

page 2

How much humus is there in the soil?

Mass of tin lid + dried soil = 28g
Mass of tin lid + baked soil = 27g
Mass of humus = 1g

$$\text{Percentage of humus} = \frac{\text{mass of humus}}{\text{mass of soil}}$$

$$= \frac{1}{10} \times \frac{1}{100} = 10\%$$

10 Soil size and porosity

Size

You need a sample of soil that has been thoroughly dried in a slow oven.

Pick out any small stones ,then grind the soil with a pestle and mortar to break up any lumps.

Weigh the sample.

Take a set of soil sieves with meshes of 2 mm, 0.2 mm and 0.02 mm (available from scientific suppliers).

Put the soil in the top sieve and shake the tower of sieves thoroughly. Children can take it in turns for about 15 minutes.

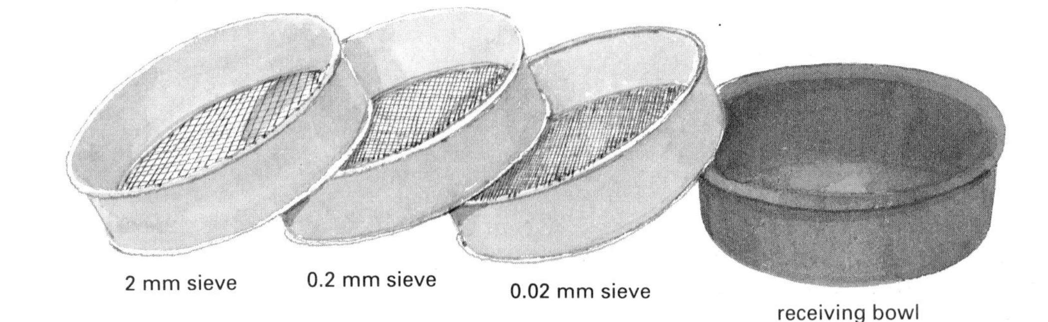

Particles from the 2 mm sieve represent gravel
Particles from the 0.2 mm sieve represent coarse sand
Particles from the 0.02 mm sieve represent fine sand
Particles in the receiving bowl represent silt plus clay

If you weigh the particles from each sieve you can work out what percentage they make of the initial mass of soil.

SOIL	DIAMETER
Coarse sand	2·0 to 0·2 mm
Fine sand	0·2 to 0·02 mm
Silt	0·02
Clay	less than 0·002 mm

Porosity

Take two identical yoghurt pots. Make a mark halfway down the side of each one in exactly the same place. Make a hole in the base of one. Cover the hole with a piece of blotting paper.

Fill the tub with the hole half full of soil to the mark. Put it in the neck of a jam jar.

Half fill the other tub with water to the mark.

Pour this water on to the soil in the tub.

How long does it take for the water to start dripping through?

How long does it take for all the water to drip through?

What colour is this water?

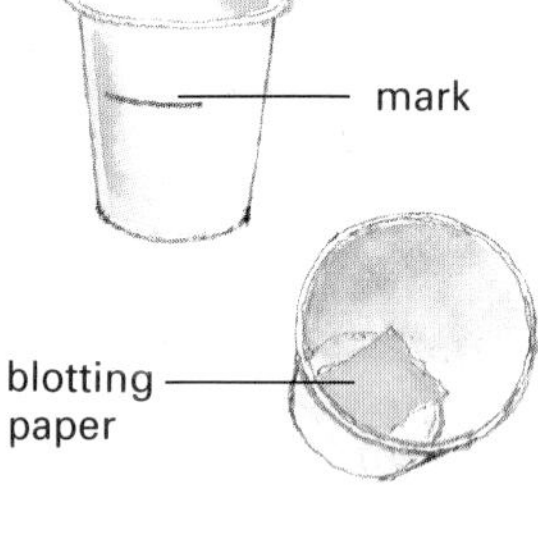

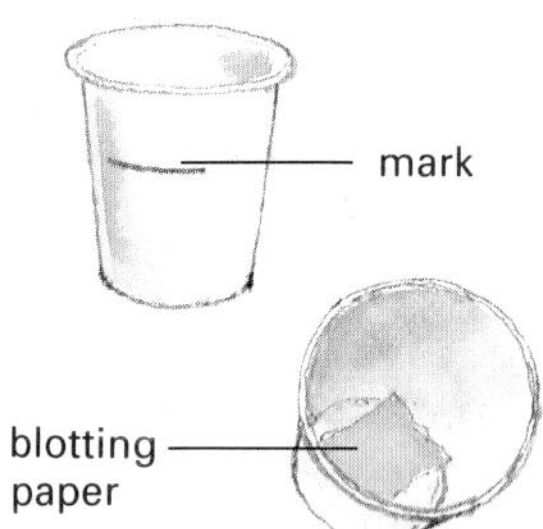

Pour the water from the jar back into the original tub.

Does it come back to the original mark?

Try different soils.
Which hold most water?
Which allow water through easily?

Some soils are acid ('sour'). Some soils are alkaline ('sweet').

Universal indicator is used to test them. Alternatively, you can also use a soil testing kit bought from a garden centre. A colour chart is used to match the colour in the test and tell how acid or alkaline the soil is.

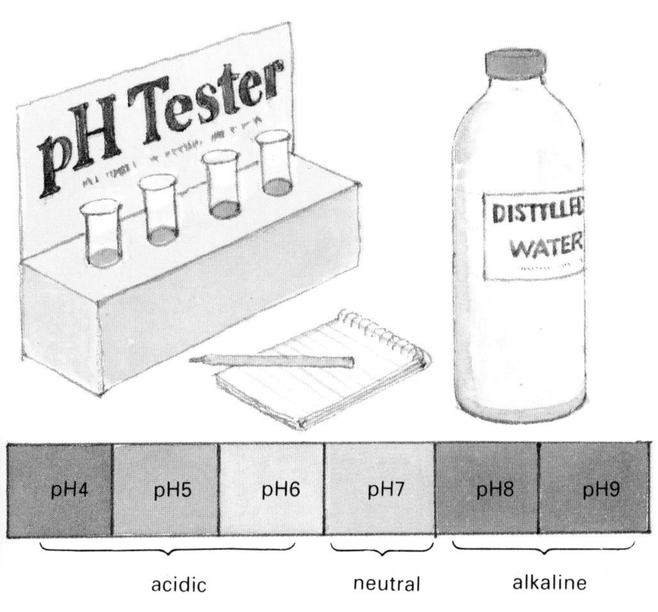

Fill about a third of a test tube with distilled water. Add a little soil from your sample. Shake. Add 2 or 3 drops of indicator. Match the colour.

Make your own indicator

You can make your own indicator by chopping and boiling red cabbage. It gives a bluish liquid.

Put about 1 cm depth of the cabbage water into two identical jars with lids.

Add white spirit vinegar to one jar drop by drop until the liquid in it goes red.

Add a spoonful of your soil sample to each jar.

Put on the lids and shake.

If your bluish liquid turns red the soil is acid. If your red liquid turns bluish the soil is alkaline.

Make a soil acidity map of the soil around the school grounds.

Adding lime

Lime makes a soil less acid, 'sweeter' as the gardener might say. Use slaked lime <u>not</u> quicklime for these tests. Be careful not to get lime on your hands or clothes in these tests.

Make a solution of distilled water and white vinegar. This is an acid solution.

Add two or three drops of universal indicator, or red cabbage water. Both will give a red solution.

Add a little lime. Shake. Keep adding lime and shaking. You should get a colour change towards the alkaline colours on the colour chart.

Lime also flocculates soil – that is to say, it causes soil particles to stick together, forming lumps which give the soil a better crumb structure and leave spaces for good aeration.

Fill two lidded jars with water. Put a tablespoon of fine clay into each. Shake the jars.

What happens?

Put a spoonful of lime in one jar. Shake both jars again and leave them to stand.

The water in the jar with lime will be clearer after a while than the water in the jar without lime.

Soil erosion

Soil is often blown away by the wind or washed away by water.

Wind erosion

This can be demonstrated with a hairdryer and various soils.

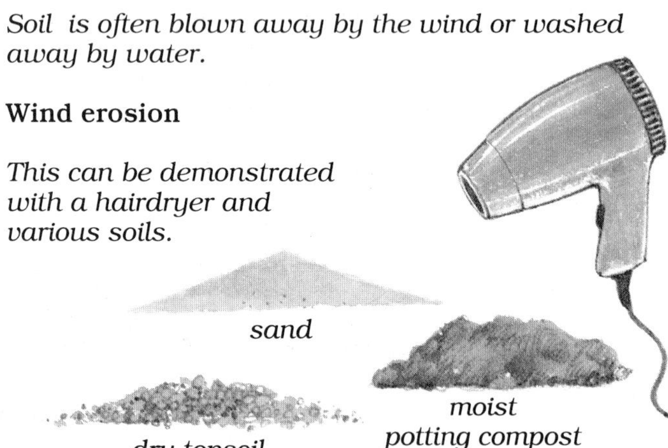

Water erosion

For all these experiments you will need thick cardboard boxes lined with plastic sheet, with a hole cut at one end.

Water washes soil away

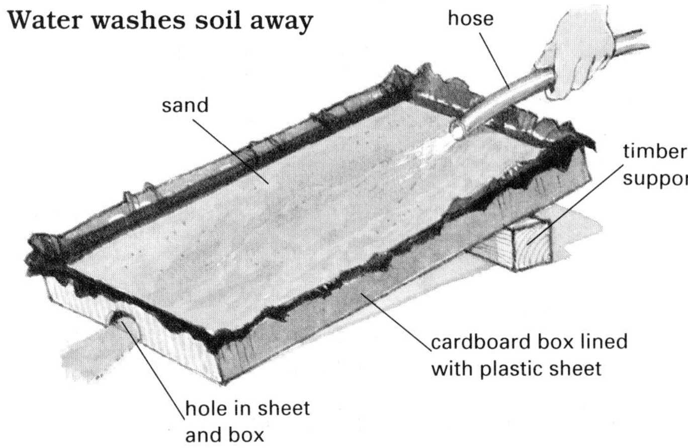

Hose the sand with water. Start gently. What happens?

Continue more vigorously. What happens?

What happens if you increase the slope of the box?

Does compactness of the soil prevent erosion?

Pour a full watering can of water on to each soil sample.

Examine what collects in the bucket each time.

What happens if you keep on watering?

Does the method of ploughing affect erosion?

Fill each box with soil but make different furrow patterns in the soils. Predict which will give greatest runoff.

Pour equal amounts of water on each.Where is there most runoff?

Try other patterns.

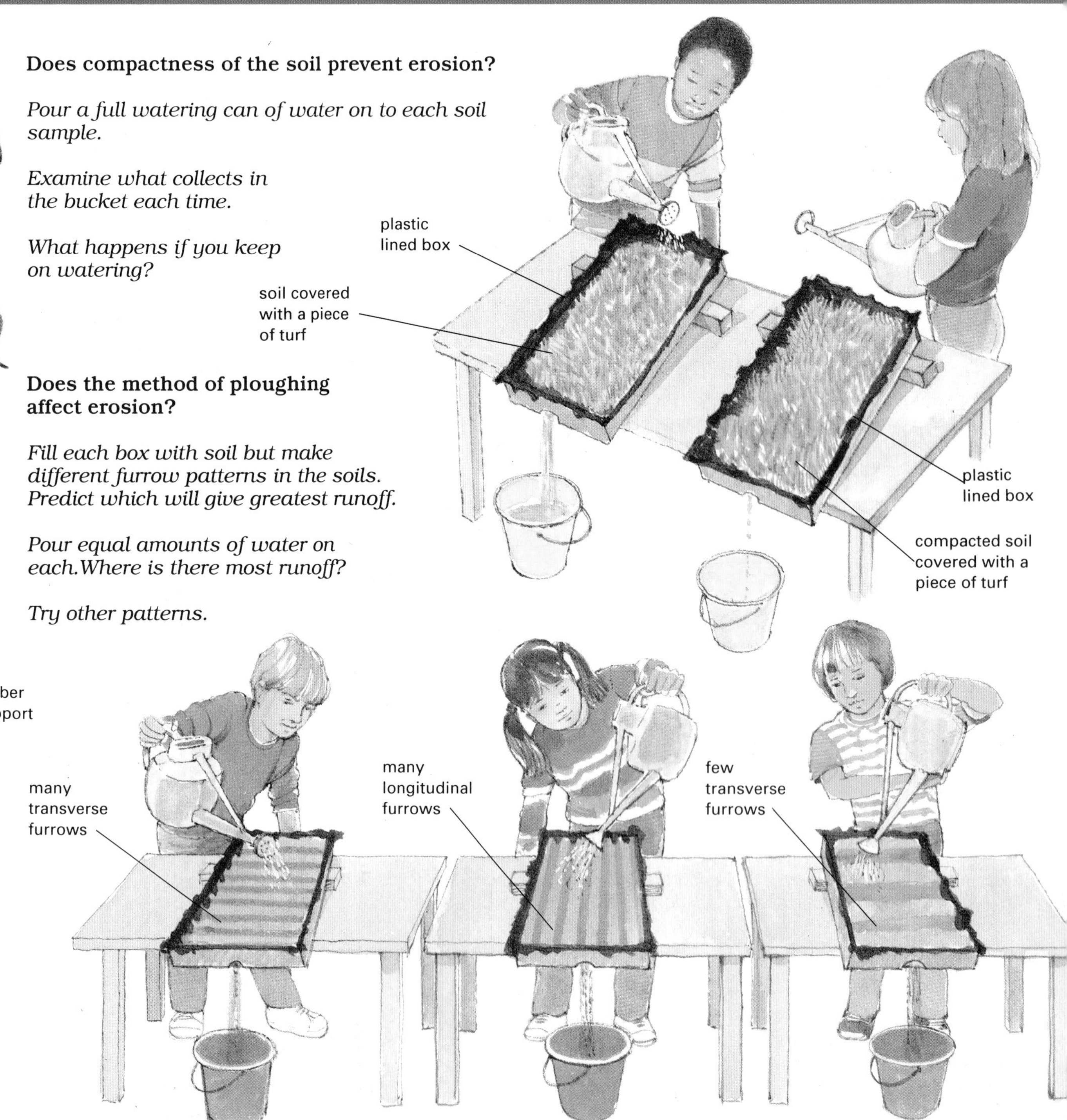

1 *Cut the tops and bottoms off some plastic bottles (2 litre lemonade bottles are ideal).*

2 *Invert the tops into the bottoms. Cut strips of cotton fabric to act as wicks.*

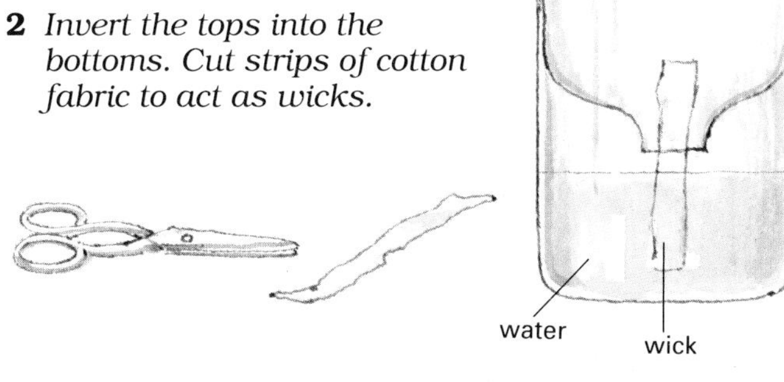
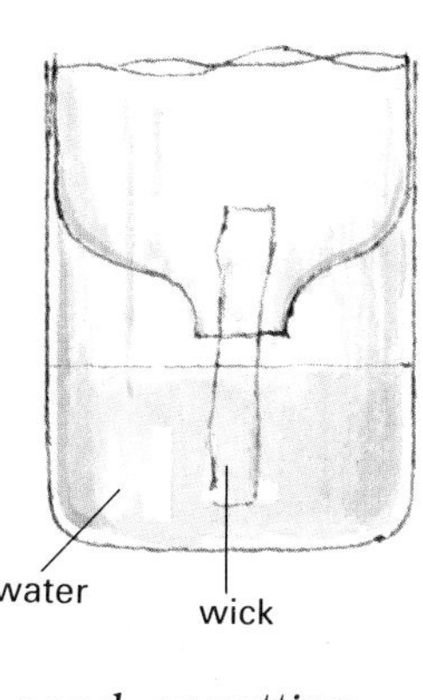

3 *Put the growing medium – soil, sand, or potting compost – into the inverted top half of each. Make sure the wick is well placed to soak up water, or water plus liquid fertilizer, from the lower half.*

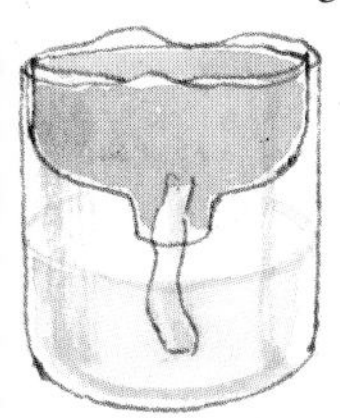
sana

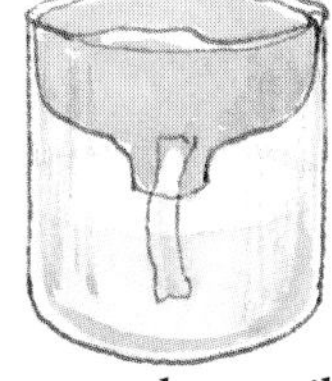
garden soil

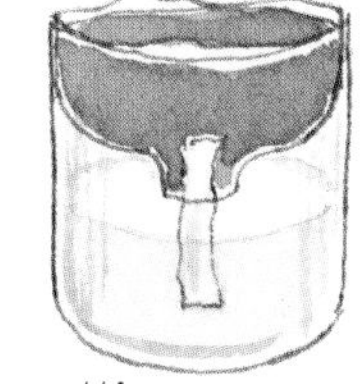

potting compost

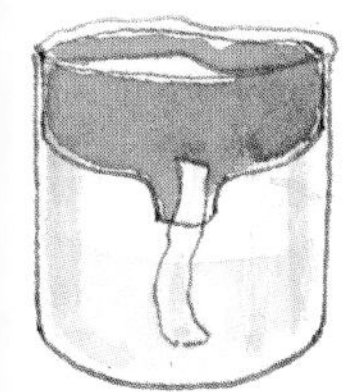
sand + liquid fertilizer

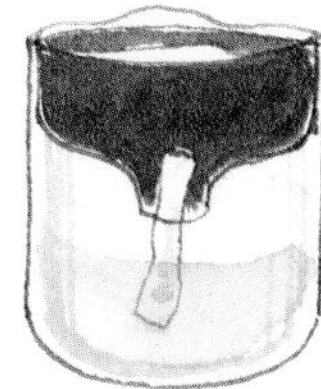
garden soil + liquid fertilizer

potting compost + liquid fertilizer

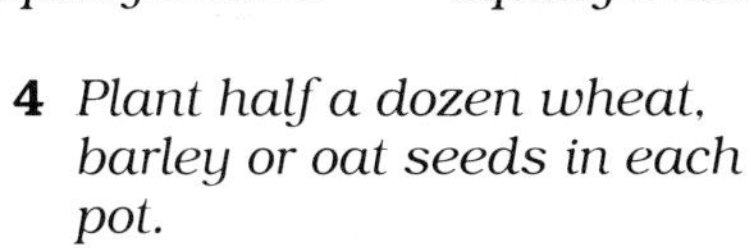

4 *Plant half a dozen wheat, barley or oat seeds in each pot.*

Mark one shoot with a fibre pen when it appears. Measure it as it grows.

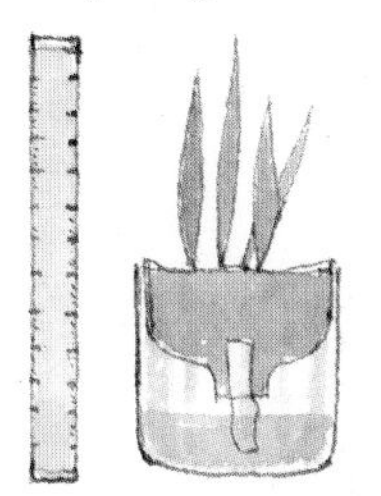

5 *Keep a record.*

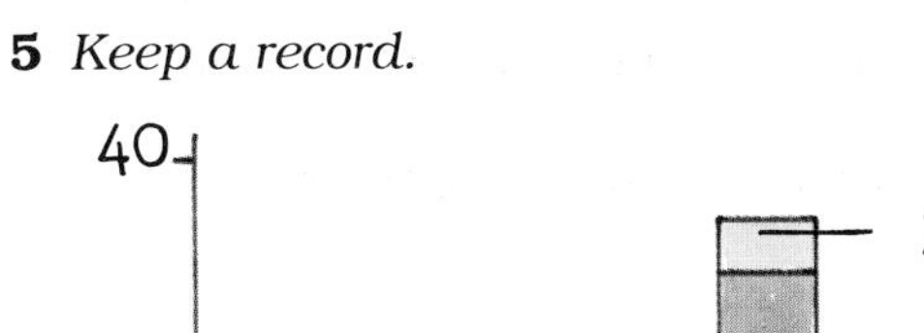
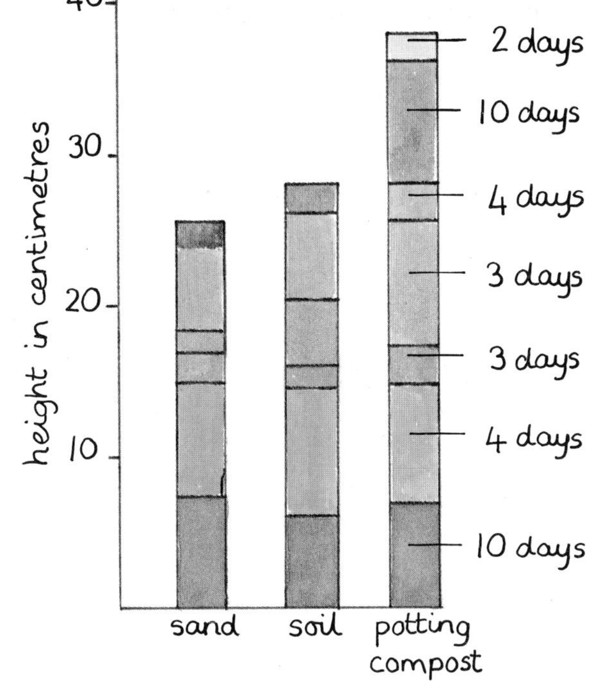

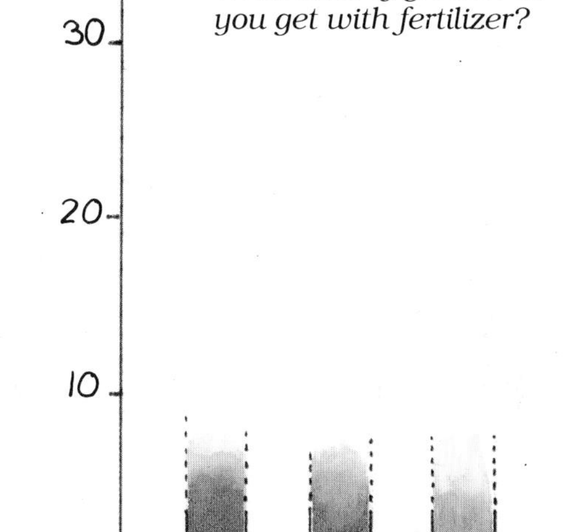

What kind of growth do you get with fertilizer?

Stick a different coloured strip of paper on the graphs for each period of time that you take a reading. The readings need not be at regular intervals – when you remember will do!

6 *Try different amounts of liquid houseplant fertilizer.*

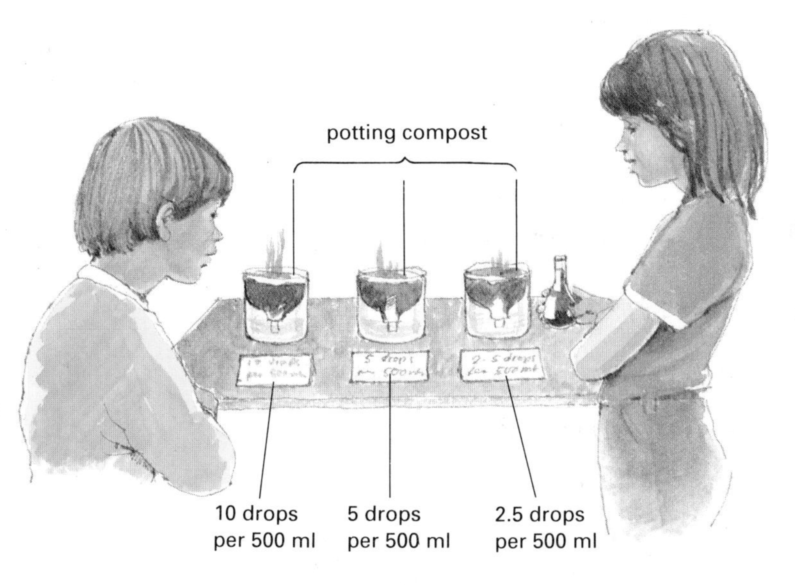

Soil shrinkage

Clay soils dry up quickly in summer, and shrink and crack.

Roll out some moist clay about 1 cm thick on a ruler. Trim the edges with a knife, so that it fits exactly and is easy to measure as it shrinks.

Leave it on a windowsill in the sun.

Measure it daily.

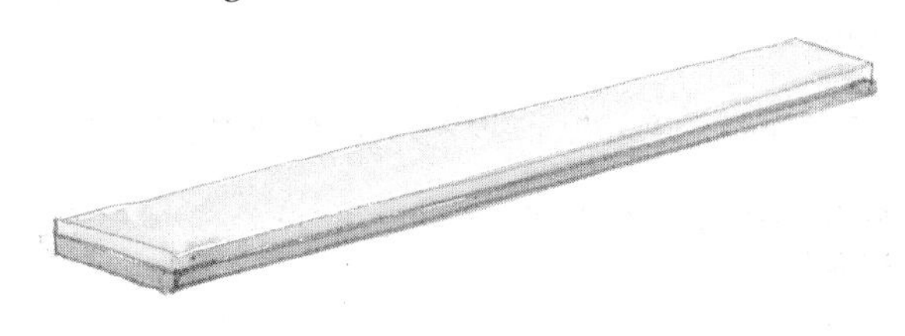

Soils and decay

Dead plant and animal material is broken down in the soil by bacterial action – it decays. The efficiency of the action depends on whether the bacteria have enough air and moisture.

One of the most familiar experiences of this process is composting garden waste. If the schoolkeeper has a compost heap it would be useful to ask him or her to show it to the children and talk to them about it.

This is a formula for a typical compost heap. It should not be too high or too compact or it will lack air. About 1 m is high enough.

20 cm plant refuse

3 cm soil with sprinkling of sulphate of ammonia to provide nitrogen

20 cm plant refuse

sprinkling of lime

20 cm plant refuse

3 cm soil with sprinkling of sulphate of ammonia

10 cm mashed tough vegetable material e.g. cabbage stalks for drainage

wire netting

Make a list of things which are suitable for the compost heap – list those which are not suitable too.

Things not suitable for a compost heap

twigs

diseased plants

tough plants

From discussion and examination of a compost heap it should be possible for children to draw up a table of the things needed for good decay.

In the natural world the bacteria would not be helped in their growth by sprinklings of nitrogenous dressing or lime. They have to start to break down plant and animal material, and get their nitrogen and calcium from that.

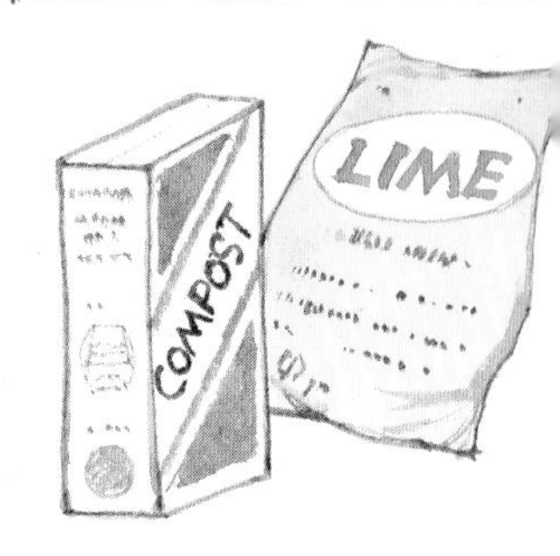

Needed for decay	
Bacteria	– in the soil
Air	– for the bacteria to respire
Water	– for the bacteria to use
Moist humus	– plant and animal material
Nitrogenous dressing	– needed by bacteria
Lime	– needed by bacteria

Great care has to be taken in dealing with a topic such as decay because of the danger of microbes.

In order to examine the effect of soil in this process it is useful to bury a range of objects. You can do this in a herbaceous border or garden plot, but it is sometimes difficult to find things afterwards!

damp soil

Select of range of hard things and bury them in damp soil inside a large biscuit tin.

Bury this just below the soil surface outdoors.

Examine the contents once a week for 3 weeks, wearing gloves.

Object	Effect		
	Week 1	Week 2	Week 3
Spoon			
Nail			
Marble			
Comic			

Observing decay

Observing the decay of plant material on the compost heap is a useful experience for children, but it is possible to observe decay of soft things at closer quarters. However, this has to be done very carefully. Use jars with tight screw top lids.

Make a hole in the top of each jar and plug it with cotton wool. This lets the air circulate but keeps microbes in the jar. Put various things in the jars.

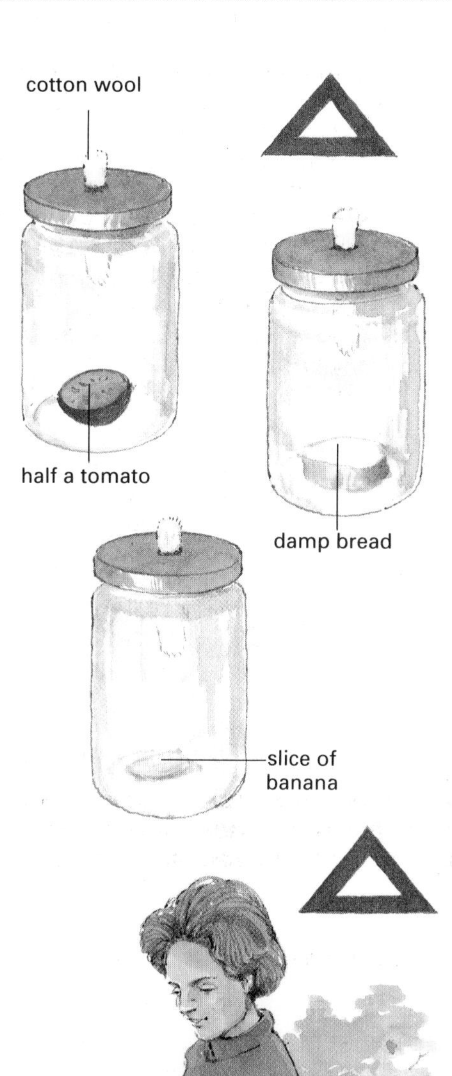

Put the jars in a warm place in the classroom, perhaps on a windowsill in the sun. Keep one or two jars with soft fruit in a cold place to investigate the effect of temperature.

Keep records for 2 to 3 weeks.

Moulds will certainly show on something like damp bread. These are fungi and they too act as agents of decay. They are saprophytes, that is to say plants that feed on decaying material.

Disposal of material

At the end of the experiment take the jar outdoors without the children present. Remove the lid and gently fill the jar with a clear disinfectant, e.g. 'Clearsol', 'Stericol', 'Sudol'. Include the cotton wool plug and leave for 24 hours. Then dispose of the contents.

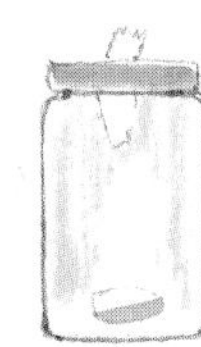

Disposal of waste – sewerage

A visit to a sewage works is useful for older juniors because all the processes are open to view and, with a good preliminary briefing, children can understand what is happening.

Waste from lavatory pans, baths and sinks passes to the sewers, as do rain and street washings and waste from factories. All this is taken to the sewage works, where bacteria play a significant part in its breakdown.

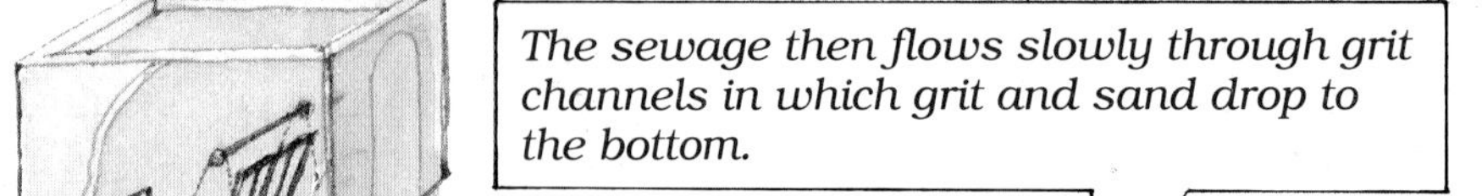

When the sewage first arrives it is passed through mesh screens to remove wood, plastic, rags and so on. This material is either cut up and returned to the flow or removed and disposed of.

The sewage then flows slowly through grit channels in which grit and sand drop to the bottom.

The sewage now passes to primary sedimentation tanks where it remains for four to six hours. Here the solids, called 'crude sludge', settle on the bottom.

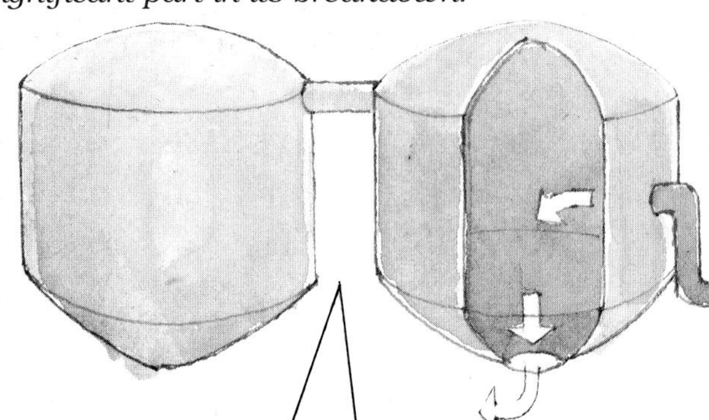

The sludge from the primary settlement tanks is pumped to digestion tanks. Here it is broken down over a two to three week period by microbes.The methane produced by this process can be used to generate the power required to run other parts of the plant. The remaining sludge, called 'digested sludge', can either be used on the land, after some of its water has been removed, or dumped at sea.

The liquid from the primary sedimentation tanks passes to aeration tanks. Here it is broken down by mixing it with compressed air and microbes. This process take about eight hours.

(At smaller works, percolating filters do the same job as the aeration tanks. Here the liquid is sprayed onto a bed of gravel in a tank, then it breaks down as it passes through the gravel.)

The liquid from the aeration tanks now passes to the final sedimentation tanks. The microbes are separated from the liquid, which is usually clean enough to be released into a river.

A sewage works can be modelled with cardboard boxes and plastic cartons. Pieces of plastic tubing can be used to simulate pipes, or jumbo art straws could be used.

Label the various parts according to the diagram on the previous page.

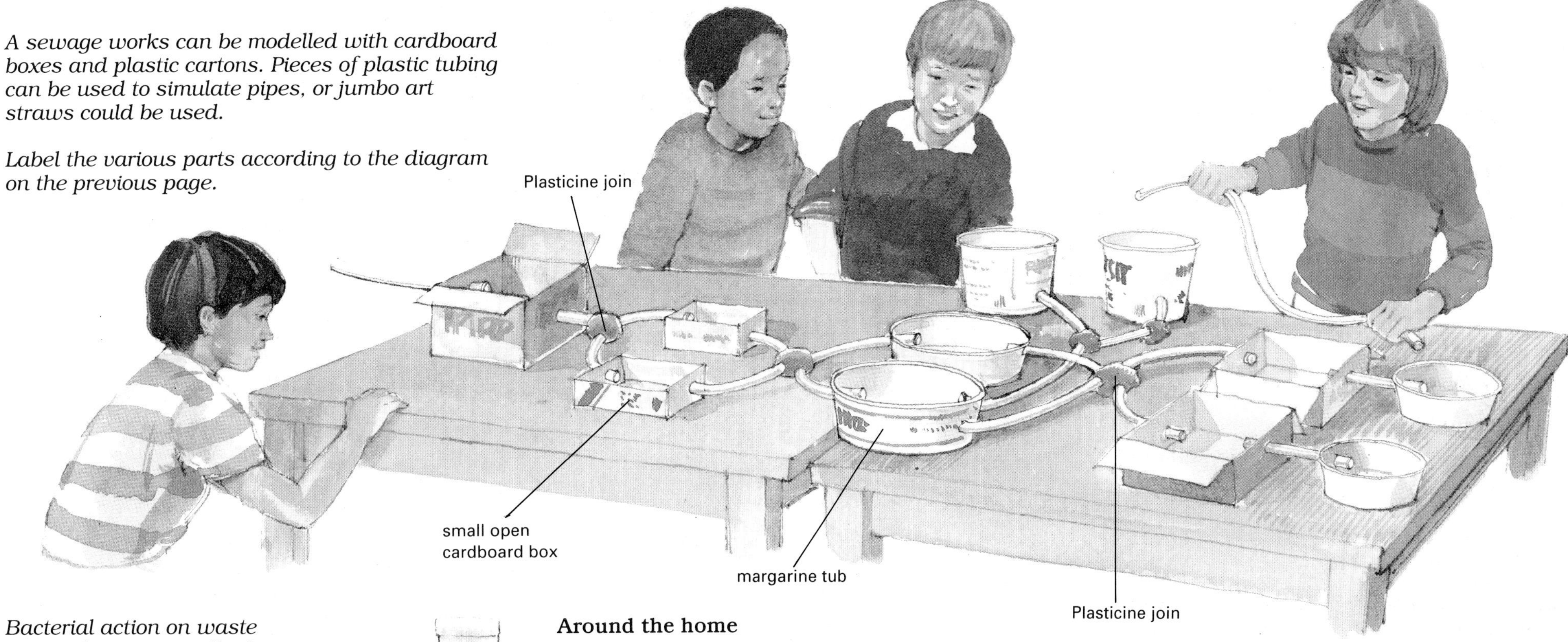

Bacterial action on waste material causes smells. In the home we have an S-bend to the lavatory pan, and under the sink, basins and bath, to prevent gases from rising from the drains. Make a model to show this.

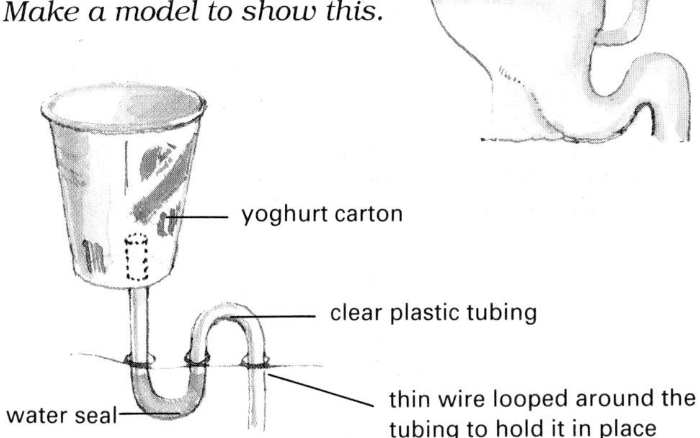

Around the home

Ask the children to look around at home and

1 *Make a sketch of how rainwater from the roof reaches the drains.*

2 *Make a rubbing of a drain cover.*

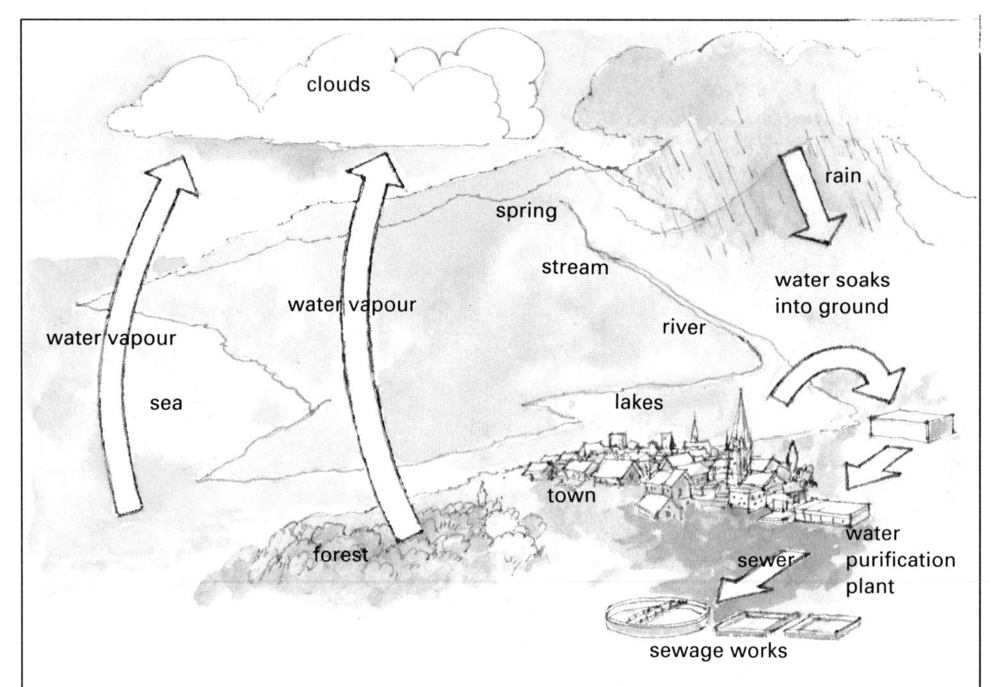

The amount of water in the world remains constant and goes through a cycle. Water evaporates from the oceans, lakes and rivers to form water laden clouds. These are moved by winds. When they reach a region of cold air the water vapour condenses and is precipitated as rain or snow. This soaks into the land and runs via streams and rivers to the sea. The water evaporates again and so the cycle is repeated over and over again.

Condensation

This can be demonstrated by causing steam from an electric kettle to hit a cold surface such as that provided by a plate or saucepan lid.

cold plate

All experiments with boiling kettles should be performed only by the teacher, wearing thick rubber gloves. One gram of steam at 100°C delivers as much heat to your skin as 5 g of iron at 1000°C.

Steam is a gas. When it cools it turns to liquid water, or to water vapour which can be thought of as tiny drops of liquid water hanging in the air. All air contains some water vapour. When there is a lot we see cloud or mist.

Warm air can hold a lot of water vapour. As air cools it can hold less, and the vapour condenses to form drops of liquid. This is what happens on the cold plate.

True steam is invisible. Look at the clear zone next to the spout of a boiling kettle. After a few centimetres it begins to condense to isible water vapour.

Holding a lit candle here extends the invisible zone, for it heats the air at this point.

Evaporation

Evaporation is a common phenomenon,but it needs discussion. It too can be demonstrated.

wet coat drying

puddles drying out after rain

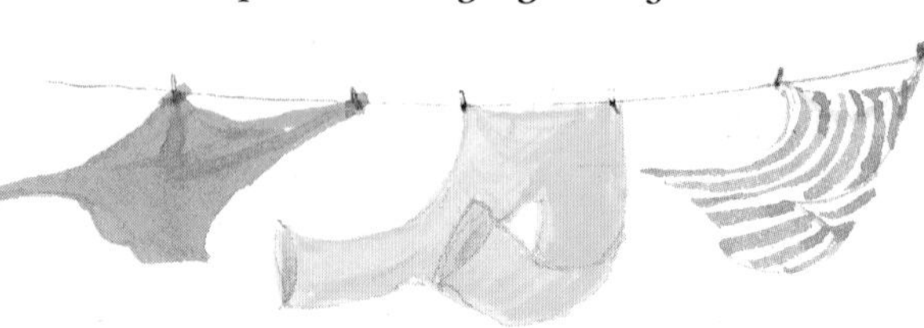

washing on a line

saucer of water on a radiator

How quick?

A good open-ended investigation is to give groups of children 20 ml of water each. Which group can devise the quickest way to get it to evaporate?

Hard water

A hard water is one which does not lather readily with soap. Hardness is caused by the presence of calcium and/or magnesium salts. These can be removed by adding soap, which makes them come off as a scum.

$Ca(HCO_3)_2$	+	$2C_{17}H_{35}COONa$	$\longrightarrow$	$Ca(C_{17}H_{35}COO)_2$	+	$2NaHCO_3$
calcium bicarbonate		sodium stearate (soap)		calcium stearate (insoluble scum)		sodium bicarbonate

Temporary hard water

This is water that can be softened by boiling.

$Ca(HCO_3)_2$	$\longrightarrow$	$CaCO_3$	+	H_2O	+	CO_2
calcium bicarbonate		calcium carbonate		water		carbon dioxide

The dissolved bicarbonate changes to the insoluble carbonate which forms the 'fur' in kettles.

fur

In the home temporary hard water can be softened by adding of washing soda (sodium carbonate).

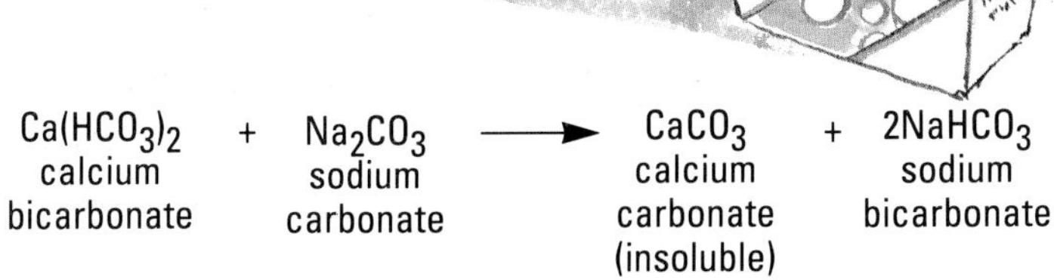

$Ca(HCO_3)_2$	+	Na_2CO_3	$\longrightarrow$	$CaCO_3$	+	$2NaHCO_3$
calcium bicarbonate		sodium carbonate		calcium carbonate (insoluble)		sodium bicarbonate

Permanent hard water

This is water that cannot be softened by boiling. The hardness is caused by chlorides and sulphates of calcium and magnesium.

Permanent hard water can be softened with washing soda.

$CaSO_4$	Na_2CO_3	$\longrightarrow$	$CaCO_3$	+	Na_2SO_4
calcium sulphate	sodium carbonate		calcium carbonate (insoluble)		sodium sulphate

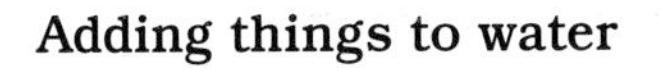

Adding things to water

Salt, sugar and washing soda dissolve in water, sand and grit do not. See 'An Early Start to Science', page 58, for activities.

Does stirring help dissolve things?

Does heat help dissolve things?

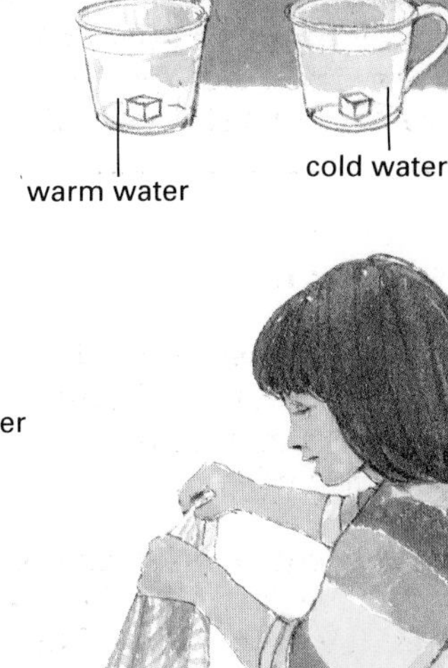

Insoluble things can be recovered by filtration; soluble things by evaporation.

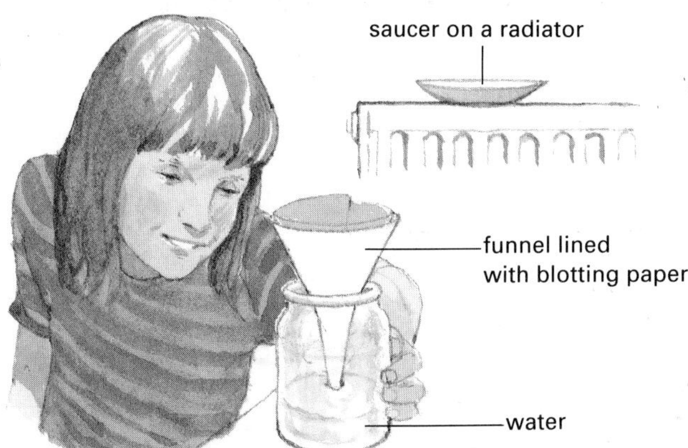

Experiments on hard and soft water and on washing things are in 'An Early Start to Technology', page 86.

Pressure and depth

Pour water through a funnel into a hose leading to a balloon. A little water creates a lot of pressure simply by its depth, and the balloon will swell. It will, of course, get quite large as more water is added.

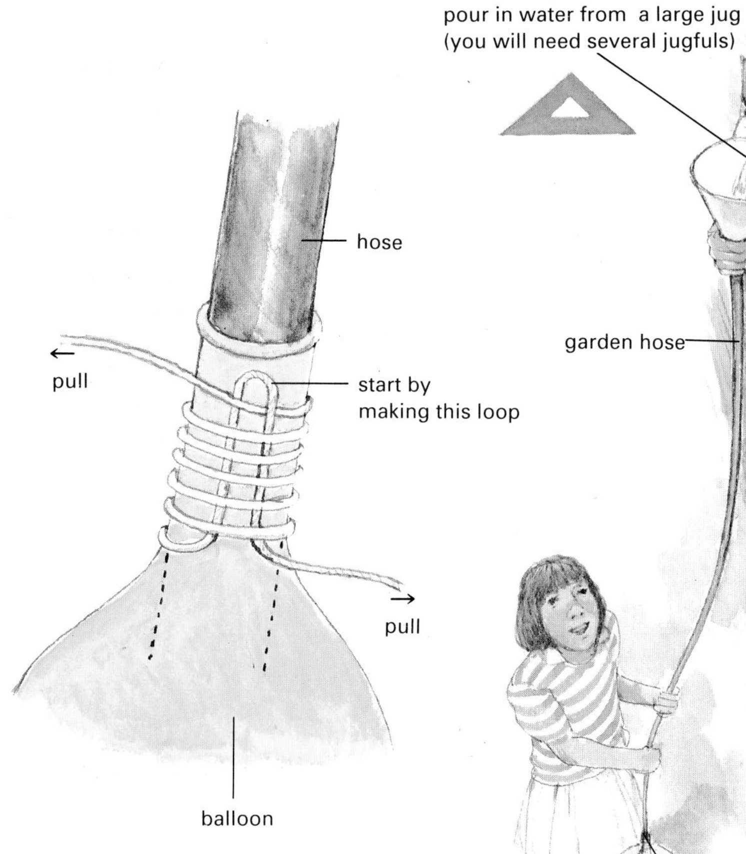

Do this outside from a first-floor window – not indoors, in case the whole thing comes undone or the balloon bursts!

Take as tall a tin as you can find and make three holes in the side using a hammer and a nail. A commercial size coffee tin is ideal. Put one hole about a third of the way from the top of the tin and another hole near the bottom. Put the third hole in between these two. Cover the holes with a strip of masking tape.

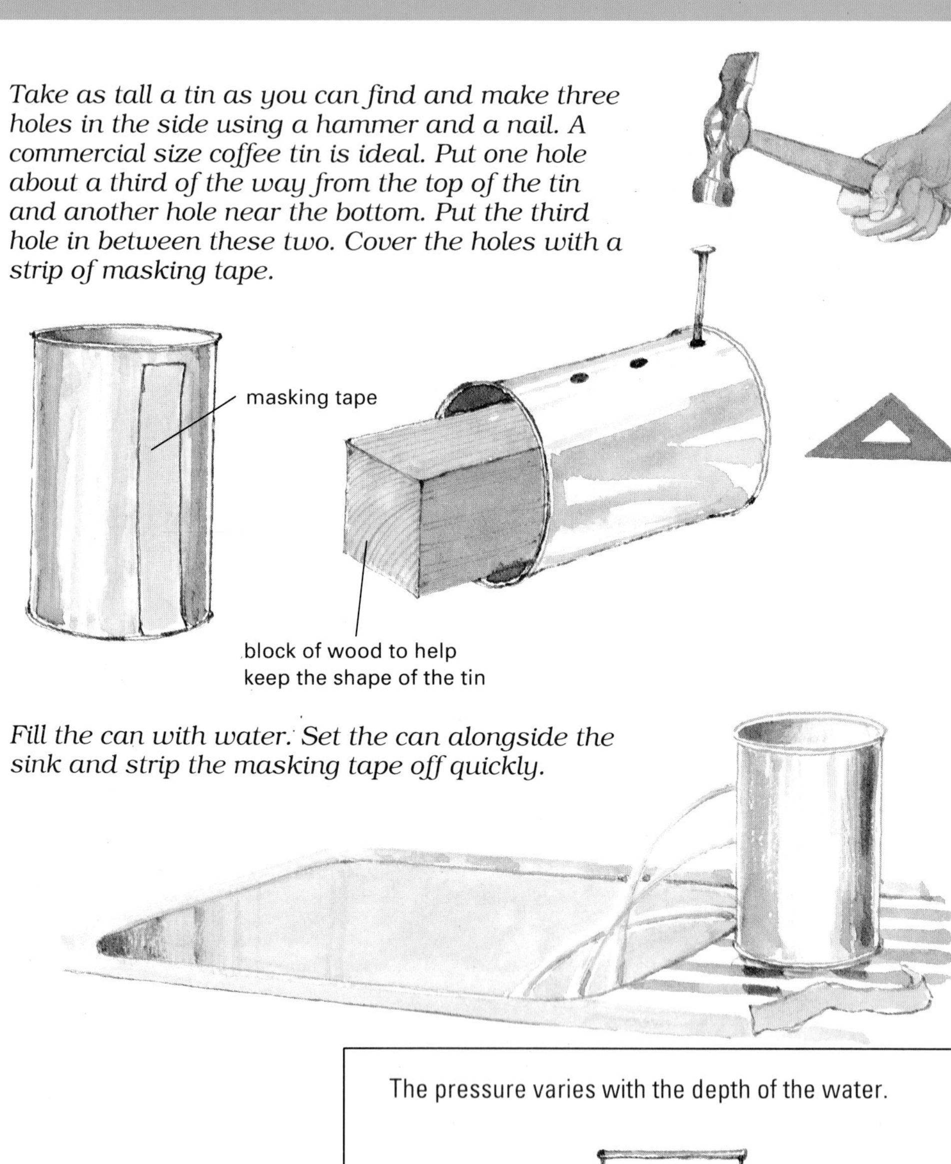

Fill the can with water. Set the can alongside the sink and strip the masking tape off quickly.

The pressure varies with the depth of the water.

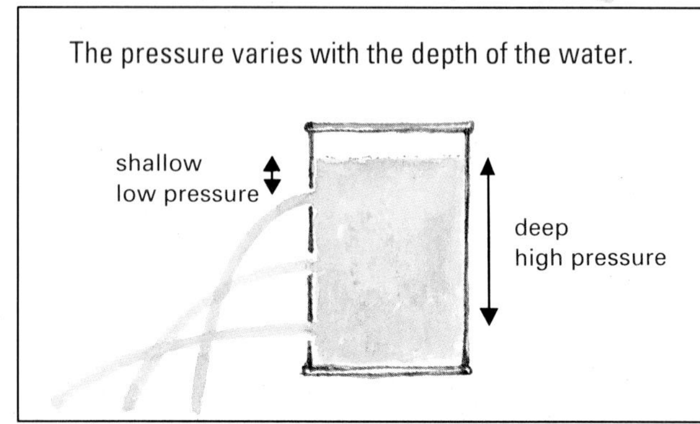

Changing pressure

Another way to show the water pressure varying with the depth is to make a ring of holes around the bottom of a tin to start.

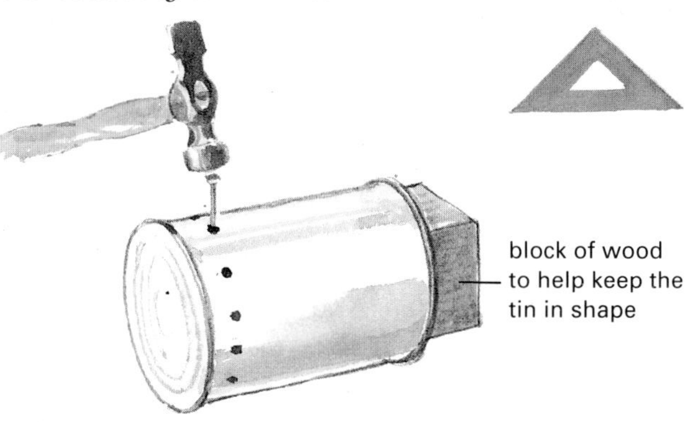

Cover the holes with masking tape. Fill the tin with water.

Hold it above the centre of the sink. Strip the masking tape away.

What happens to the jets of water as the water level in the tin falls?

Repeat the exercise but this time tilt the tin. What happens?

The push of water

By making a slight variation to the tin you can use the water running out to make the tin spin.

Put the nail in each hole in the tin in turn and pull it sharply to one side. Try to keep the pull equal as you go from hole to hole.

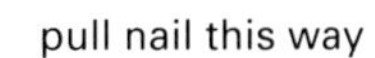

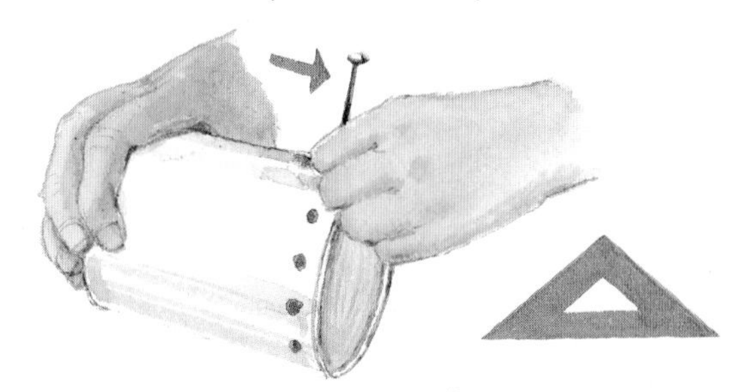

Hang the tin on a string. Cover the holes with masking tape. Fill the can with water. Strip the tape away and the tin will spin.

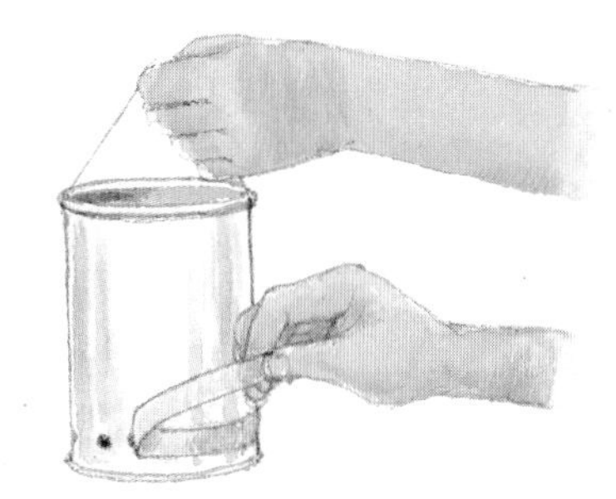

Water level

What happens as you raise and lower the plastic bottles?

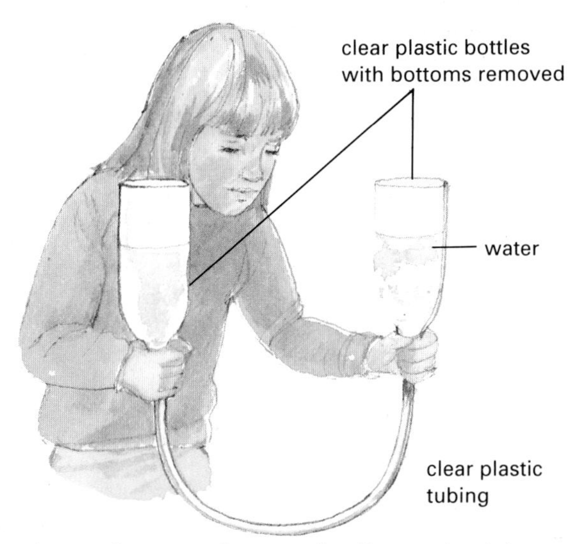

What do you have to do to make the water jet bigger? What do you have to do to make the water jet smaller?

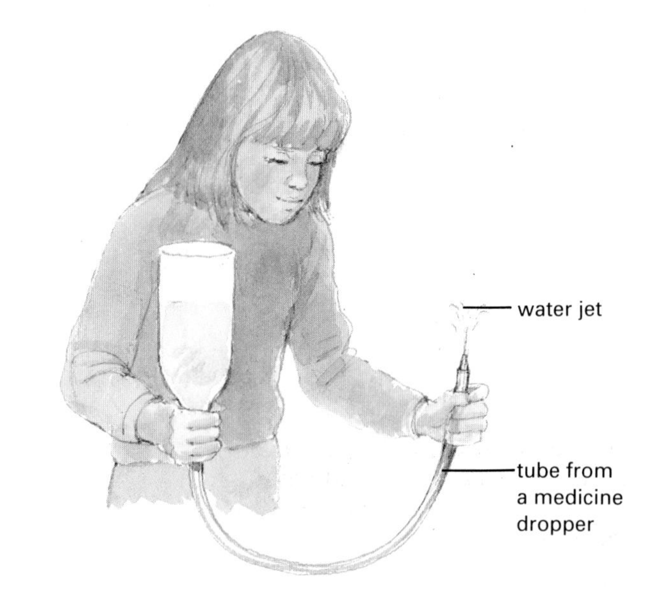

Water molecules attract each other slightly. The attractive force acts in all directions.

At the surface there is nothing for the upward part of the force to act on, so instead it acts sideways.

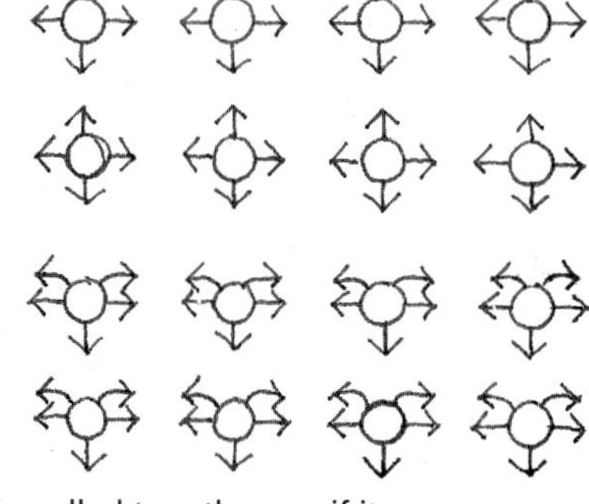

The result is that the surface of the water is pulled together, as if it were covered with an invisible elastic film—but in fact there is no film, only ordinary water. The surface force, surface tension, is strong enough to support insects and small objects. It also gives drops of water their round shape.

The following activities give children experience of surface tension.

Pond animals

Look for pond animals that use this surface tension.

whirligig beetle
Gyrinus

Gnat larvae hang from the surface of the water

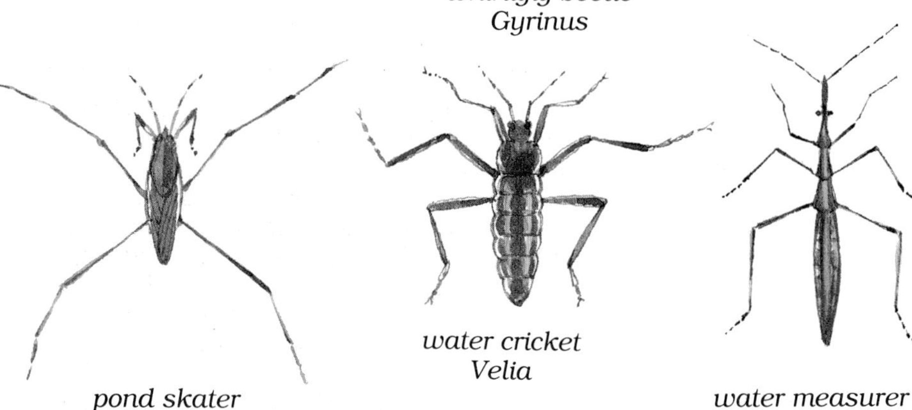

pond skater
Gerris

water cricket
Velia

water measurer
Hydrometra

See 'An Early Start to Nature', pages 52–5, for work on pond animals.

Testing surface tension

Fill a tumbler with water.
Add more very gently!

How far above the lip of the glass can you get the water before the surface tension breaks?

Start with a glass that is full to the brim with water.

Slide 10p coins in gently from the side.

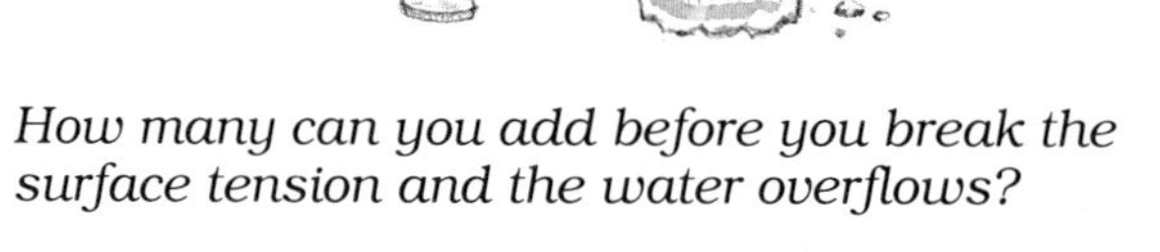

How many can you add before you break the surface tension and the water overflows?

Dry a small steel needle thoroughly. Balance it on a dinner fork.

Very gently lower it on to the surface of the water in a dish. Remove the fork.

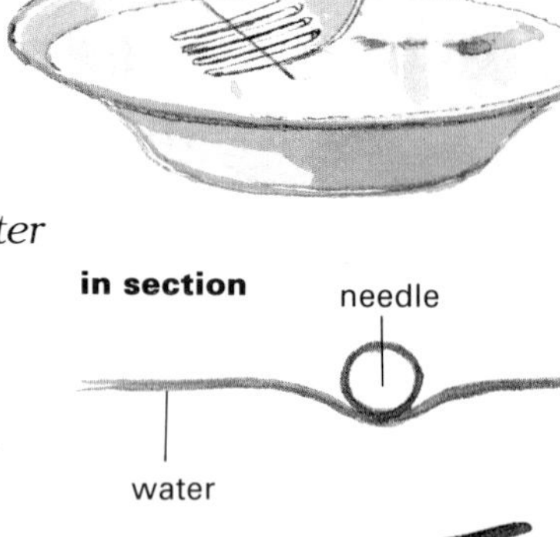

With luck, the needle will float on the water.

If you look sideways at the needle you will see the surface bending under the weight of the needle.

If you have difficulty floating the needle in this way, try floating it on a raft of tissue paper (5×2 cm). After several minutes the tissue will sink, leaving the needle floating.

Dip a paintbrush into water.

Note how the surface tension holds the hairs together when it is withdrawn from the water.

Surface tension on the move

Make four or five holes close together in the base of a tin can.

Fill the can with water from a bucket.

Hold it up.

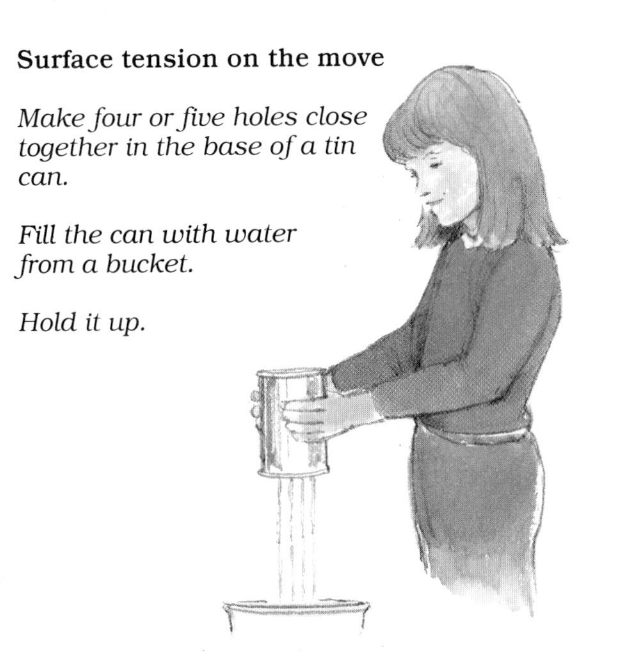

The water jets will flow out.

Now twist the jets together with your fingers.

Take your fingers away.

The surface tension will hold the jets together.

Drops of water

Put drops of water on to a ceramic tile. Note how they stand up.

Try soapy water, clear honey, clear honey and soap, cooking oil, oil and soap, turpentine or white spirit etc.

Make careful drawings of what you see.

Which can you pile highest in a jar?
Water?
Soapy water?
Cooking oil?

Surface tension allows the liquid in a jar to build up above the rim without overflowing. Other forces are: the wetting power of that liquid on a particular surface – how strongly the water is attracted to the surface – which opposes surface tension; the mass of the liquid, which depends on its density, and also opposes surface tension; and the viscosity – 'thickness' – of the liquid, which influences the speed with which a large drop sags out of shape. In the long run, two drops of liquids with equal surface tension, wetting power and density but different viscosities will end up the same shape.

Floating and sinking is a difficult area of study, for any true understanding of it demands an understanding of Archimedes' Principle, which is usually well beyond children of primary school age.

The following pages attempt an explanation of the phenomena involved in floating and sinking, and outline experiences that will help to lead children to an understanding of Archimedes' Principle when they are in secondary school.

SOME REASONS WHY OBJECTS FLOAT

These are separated here for explanation purposes, but a number of them may be operating at any one time.

Because of low density

One way of comparing substances is by how 'heavy' they are.
To compare substances properly requires taking the same volume of each substance; or, put another way,

$$\text{density} = \frac{\text{mass}}{\text{volume}}$$

Here is a table of density values.

Substance	Density (g/cm^3)	Substance	Density (g/cm^3)
Gold	19.32	Aluminium	2.70
Mercury	13.53	Glass	2.6
Lead	11.34	Carbon (graphite)	2.25
Copper	8.94	Water	1.00
Iron	7.86	Softwood	0.60
Carbon (diamond)	3.53	Cork	0.25

Note that the density of water is such that each cm^3 (ml) has a mass of 1g. Its density is thus 1g /cm^3.

Substances with a density less than that of water will float in water. Those with a density greater than that of water will sink.

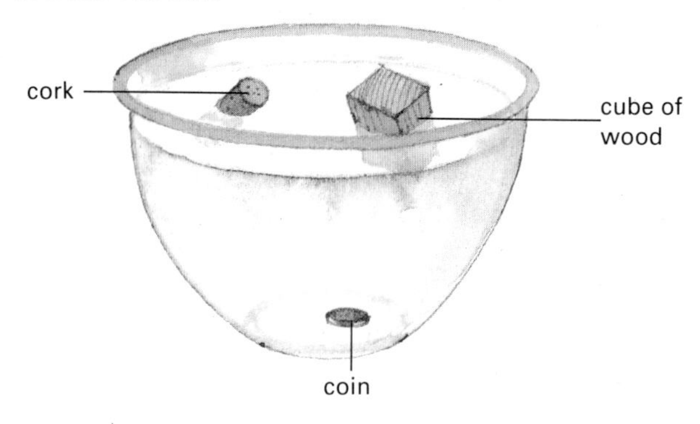

Because they are helped by having air in them

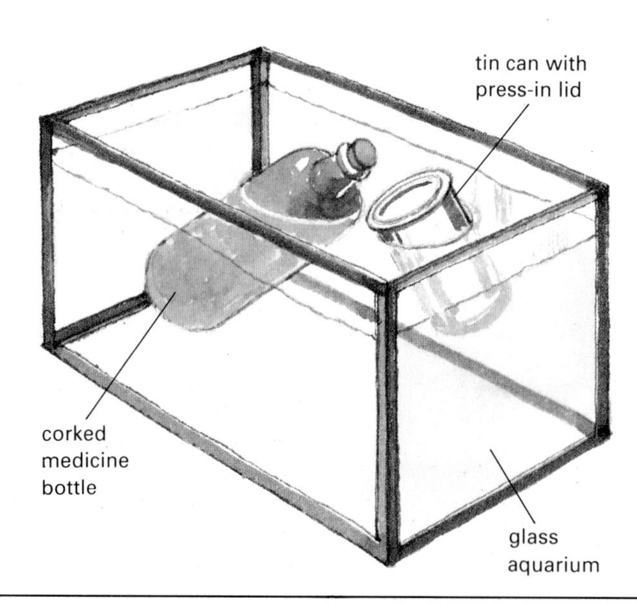

But some things with air in them will sink, e.g. a breezeblock.

Because of surface tension

See pages 22-23.

Because of differences in pressure

This block of heavy hardwood is floating just below the water surface. The pressure becomes greater the deeper one goes in the water (see page 20). The pressure underneath the block is greater than the pressure above it. The sideways forces balance each other, leaving an upward thrust on the block.

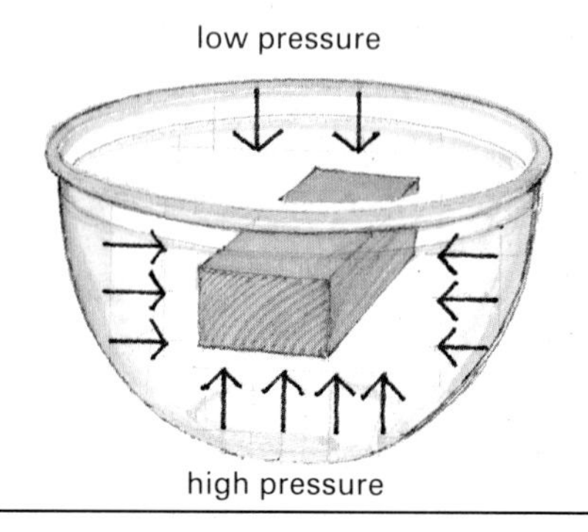

Archimedes' principle

Archimedes discovered that if an object is totally immersed in water it displaces its own volume of water. It is said that he thought of this in his bath and leapt out shouting 'Eureka'—which is a Greek way of saying 'I've found the answer'.

Archimedes did a lot of work on the upward thrust of liquid on objects immersed in water and other liquids.

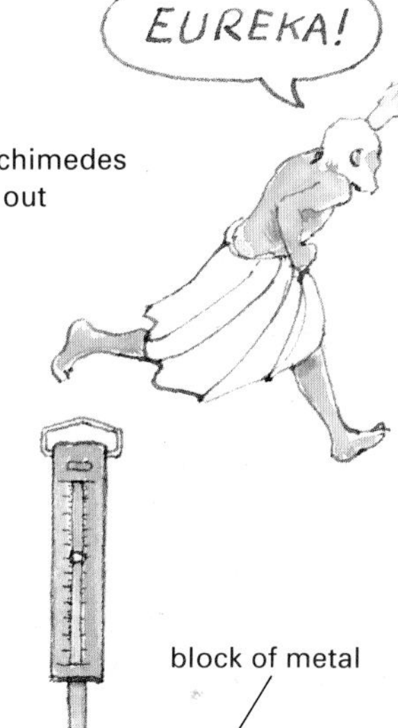

The classic experiment

To find the upward force of a liquid on an object you need to find the weight of the liquid displaced by the object. Traditionally in physics this is shown by the following experiment.

The object is weighed on a spring balance. It is lowered into water in a displacement can. The balance reading becomes less because the water is causing an upthrust on the object. The decrease is the size of this force. The weight of water displaced can be read from the dial balance. Archimedes says that the weight of this water will be equal to the upthrust.

If an object is immersed or partially immersed in a fluid, the upward force is equal to the weight of fluid displaced.

block of metal

displacement can

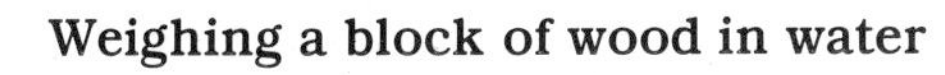

Weighing a block of wood in water

If a block of wood is attached to a spring balance and lowered into water, as the wood becomes more deeply immersed, the reading of the spring balance decreases. That is to say, the weight of water displaced and thus the upthrust of the water on the wood is increasing. Eventually the spring balance will register zero.

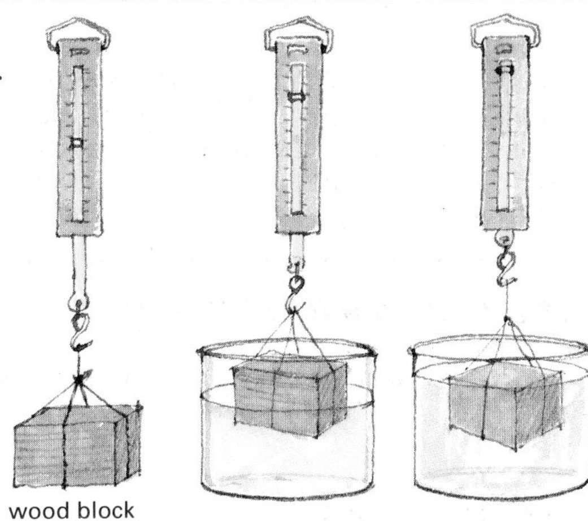

The wood block is floating because the upthrust (the upward force) in equal to its own weight.

When a body floats it displaces a weight of liquid exactly equal to its own weight.

Iron ships

Iron, even when completely immersed, displaces a weight of water less than its own weight. It therefore sinks.

Iron ships float because they are hollow, and full of air. The effective density of the ship is the mass of the iron and the large amount of air it encloses, divided by the volume of both.

A ship can, of course, be overloaded. If it is, it will lie dangerously low in the water so that waves may break over it and flood it. The Plimsoll markings on its side show how deep it may be allowed to lie in various sea conditions. The bottom mark is for the roughest sea. In fact these marks are measures of mass, like the marks on a spring balance. Plimsoll markings are shown in 'An Early Start to the Environment', page 83.

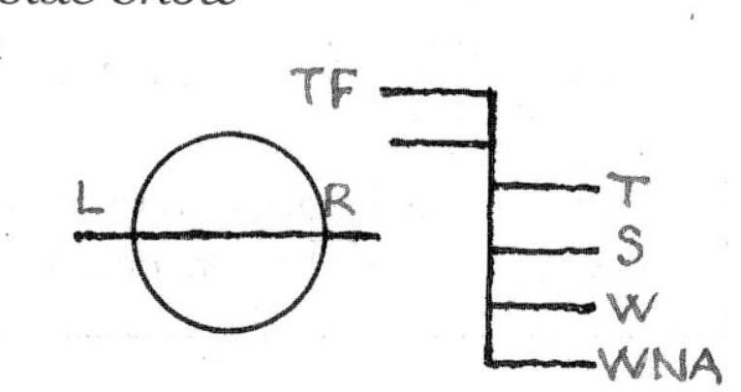

Practical experiments

The previous two pages will have shown how complex are the issues involved in floating and sinking. Young children can sort out objects that float and sink but often give wrong explanations of why they float or sink, or fail to understand what is happening. Cup shaped objects can cause confusion because displacement is involved. Pieces of kitchen foil or grains of sand can cause confusion because of surface tension effects holding them up.

One can go on and on with factors that might be involved and which might cause confusion. What is important is to present children with a variety of experiences so that understanding will eventually develop.

Here are some activities.

Lumps of things

Begin with lumps of things. It avoids any confusion over shape or whether things are hollow. Don't include things that will absorb water.

Suitable objects and materials to investigate:

- *blocks and pieces of wood of all kinds (include a piece of lignum vitae, the heavy black wood used for the 'woods' in the game of bowls—this is denser than water)*
- *rocks and pebbles*
- *metals*
- *glass, e.g. marbles*
- *plastics, e.g. expanded polystyrene, solid plastic toy*
- *rubber ball*
- *lumps of Plasticine*

Keep a record.

Floats		Sinks	
High	Low	Slowly	Quickly

Moulding Plasticine

Moulding Plasticine into cuplike shapes makes it float.

Experiment with different shapes.

Experiment with loads in the Plasticine boats.

See 'An Early Start to Technology', page 47, for experiments with Plasticine and aluminium foil boats.

How do weight and volume affect floating?

Experiment with pebbles or marbles in a sealed plastic bottle.

How does changing the number of pebbles affect the way the bottle floats?

Where are the pebbles when the bottle floats?

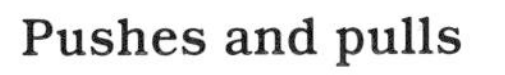

Keep a record.

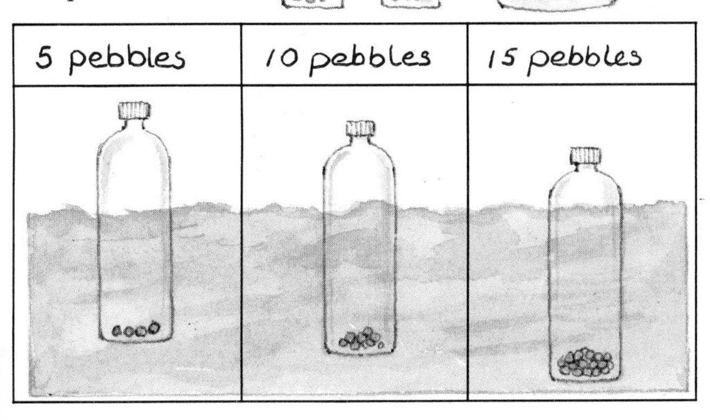

5 pebbles	10 pebbles	15 pebbles

A 'submarine'

Cut two holes near the base of a plastic bottle. Keep its cap on.

Load it with pebbles and put it into a bucket of water so that it sinks but stands upright on its base.

Insert a 1.5 m length of plastic tubing. Blow.

The bottle should rise and float.

If it is too heavy remove a few pebbles.

Pushes and pulls

It is helpful to draw children's attention to the pushes and pulls involved in floating and sinking in order to help them get a feeling for displacement.

Lower a large block of wood (1 kg) held in a net (like the one oranges are bought in) into water.

How does the block feel in air?

How does it feel as it enters the water?

How does it feel as it goes deeper into the water?

What happens to the water level in the bucket?

Tie a small rock to a sealed plastic bottle so that it floats in water.

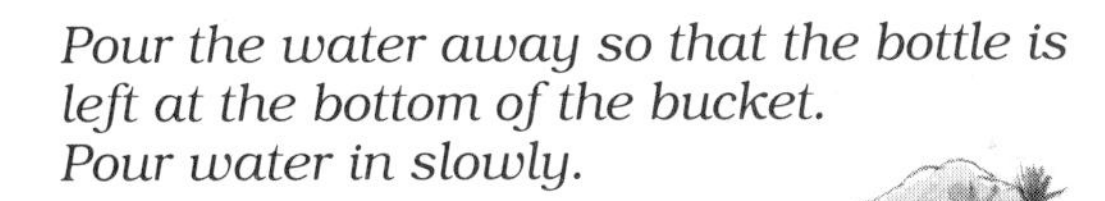

Pour the water away so that the bottle is left at the bottom of the bucket. Pour water in slowly.

What happens to the bottle?

What happens to the rock?

Try it with larger rocks.

Lower a block of wood into a completely full bucket so that children can see the water that is displaced as it floats.

Do this outdoors, of course!

Plants which do not have flowers

Algae

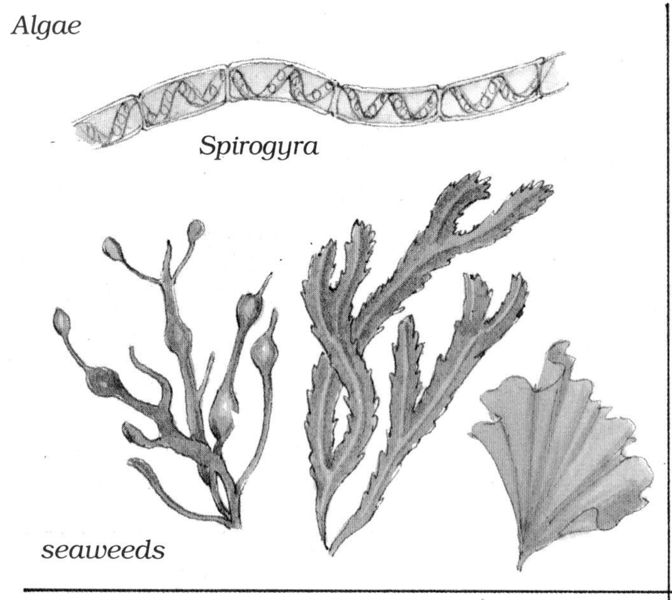

Fungi†

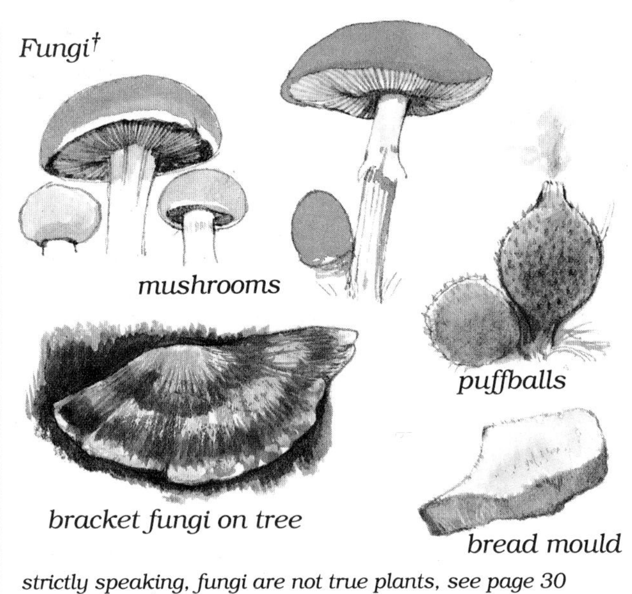

† strictly speaking, fungi are not true plants, see page 30

Lichens

Liverworts

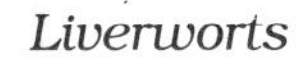

Mosses

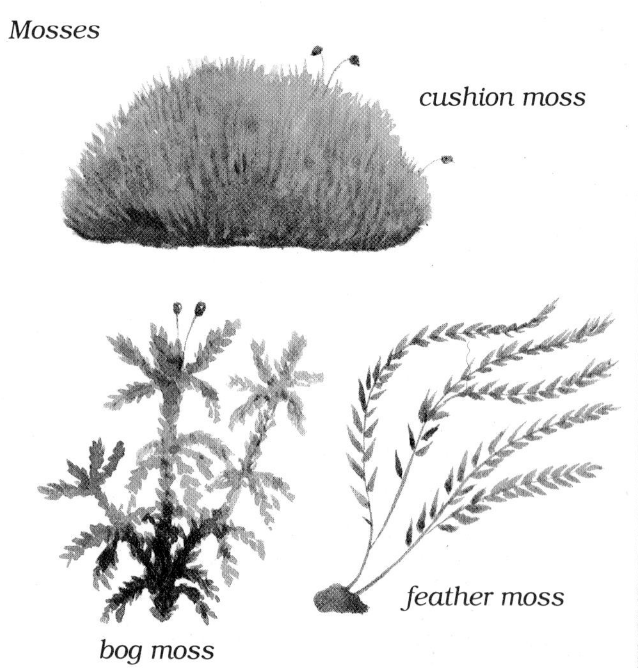

Ferns

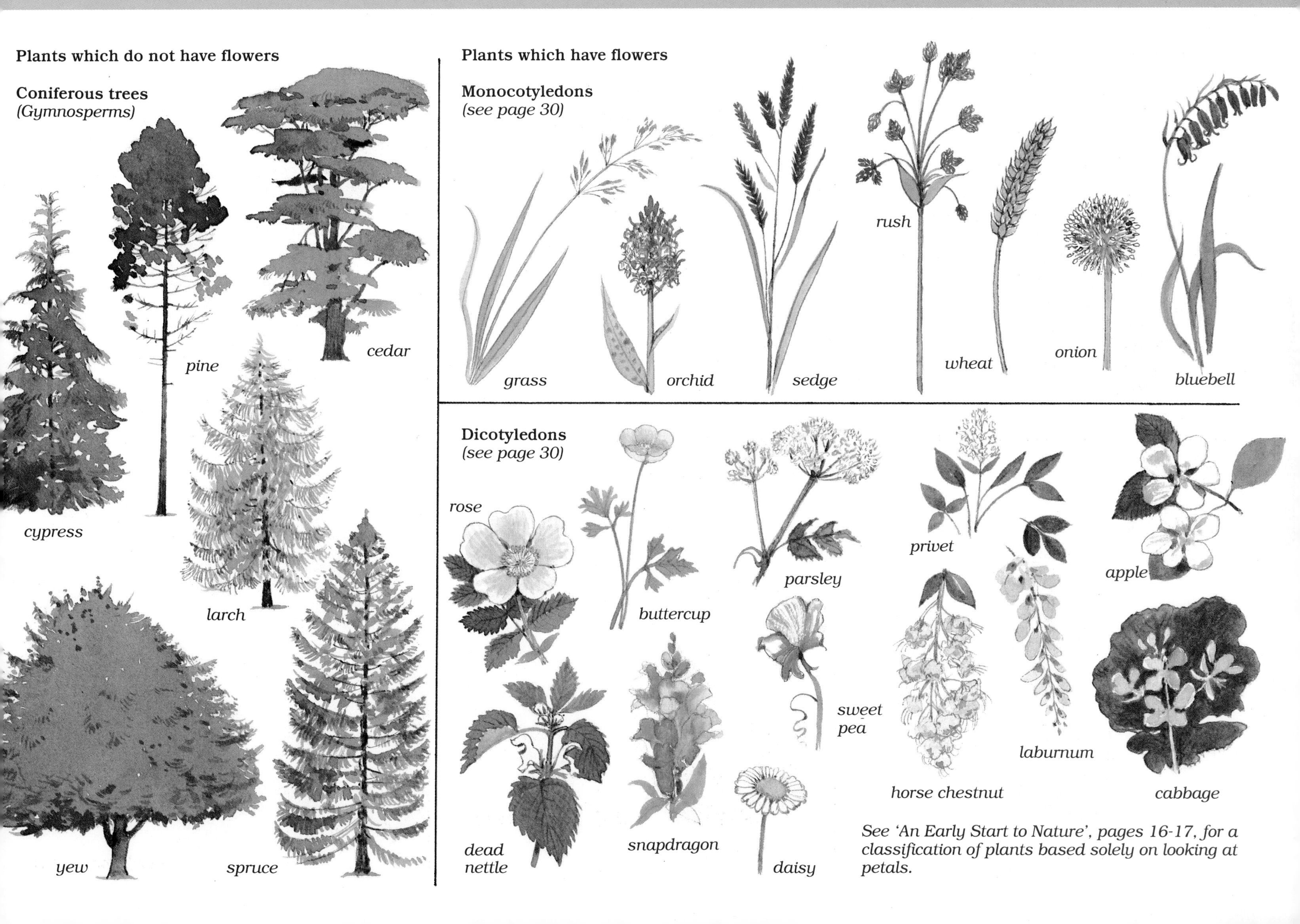

See 'An Early Start to Nature', pages 16-17, for a classification of plants based solely on looking at petals.

Plants without flowers

Algae

All contain chlorophyll, the green pigment which is necessary for photosynthesis, but it is often masked by other pigments as in the brown and red seaweeds. Some algae are single celled, but there is a range right up to complex ones such as the seaweeds. *Spirogyra*, the green slimy filaments found in ponds, is a common alga as are the seaweeds.

Fungi

These are not true plants – they have no chlorophyll and hence cannot make their own food. They must live as saprophytes, that is to say on decaying material which is made into a 'liquid' for ingestion, or as parasites. The main body is usually made of branching thread-like parts called hyphae. Pinmoulds, yeasts, mildews, mushrooms, bracket fungi.

Lichens

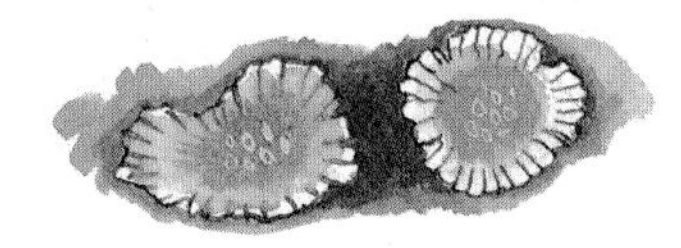

These are composite organisms consisting of an alga and a fungus living in an association which both benefit from, that is to say in symbiosis. Encrusting growths on rocks and rooftops are common. *Rhizocarpon, Lecanora, Parmelia, Xanthoria, Cladonia.*

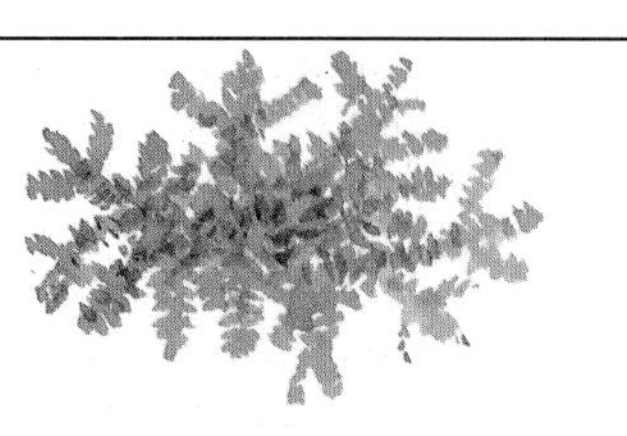

Liverworts

Small, flat, green leaf-like plants found in clusters, or ribbons, in damp places. *Pellia, Lophocolea, Lunularia.*

Mosses

Small leafy plants with the leaves spirally arranged on the stem. Commonly found in compact cushions or as a carpet. *Funaria, Sphagnum, Byrum.*

Ferns

These have well developed roots and a transporting system to carry nutrients through their tissues. There are two generations in the life history of a fern: a small, short lived plant which produces gametes; and a large, spore producing plant which in many instances lives several years. Male fern, maidenhair fern, bracken, hart's tongue fern, royal fern.

Gymnosperms

The ovules and seeds are naked–i.e. they are not found in a seed box. Pine, larch, cedar, yew, cypress

Plants with flowers

Monocotyledons

Narrow leaved plants with only one cotyledon ('seed leaf') in their seeds. Grasses, rushes, sedges, lily and orchid families.

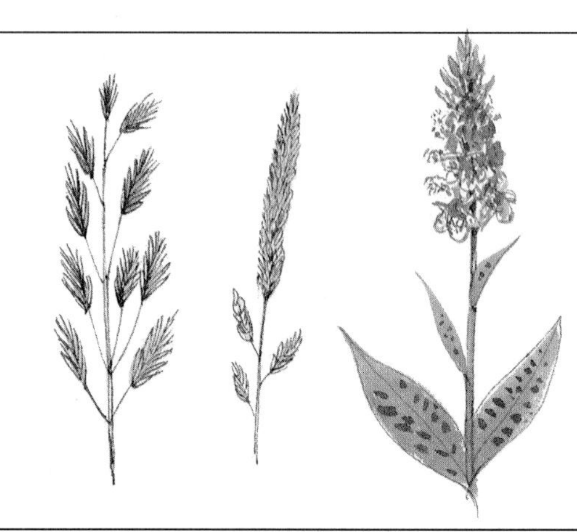

Dicotyledons

Broad leaved plants with two cotyledons in their seeds. Herbaceous plants such as dandelion, daisy, buttercup, sweetpea. Shrubs such as blackthorn, privet, box. Deciduous trees such as oak, horse chestnut, ash, lime, hazel, beech and apple. Non-deciduous or evergreen trees such as holly, laurel, magnolia and box.

The ability to sort living things into broad groups according to observable features is an important one for children to develop. It comes from collecting, observing and investigating plants and animals, the majority of which will be found near the school and home. Such observations will eventually enable children to mark living things against keys using observable features of organisms.

Identification usually begins by matching living things against clear pictures in books.

Keys

Eventually more precise methods are needed and children learn to use keys. The idea of a key is easy to establish by taking almost any collection of objects and sorting it according to paired criteria.

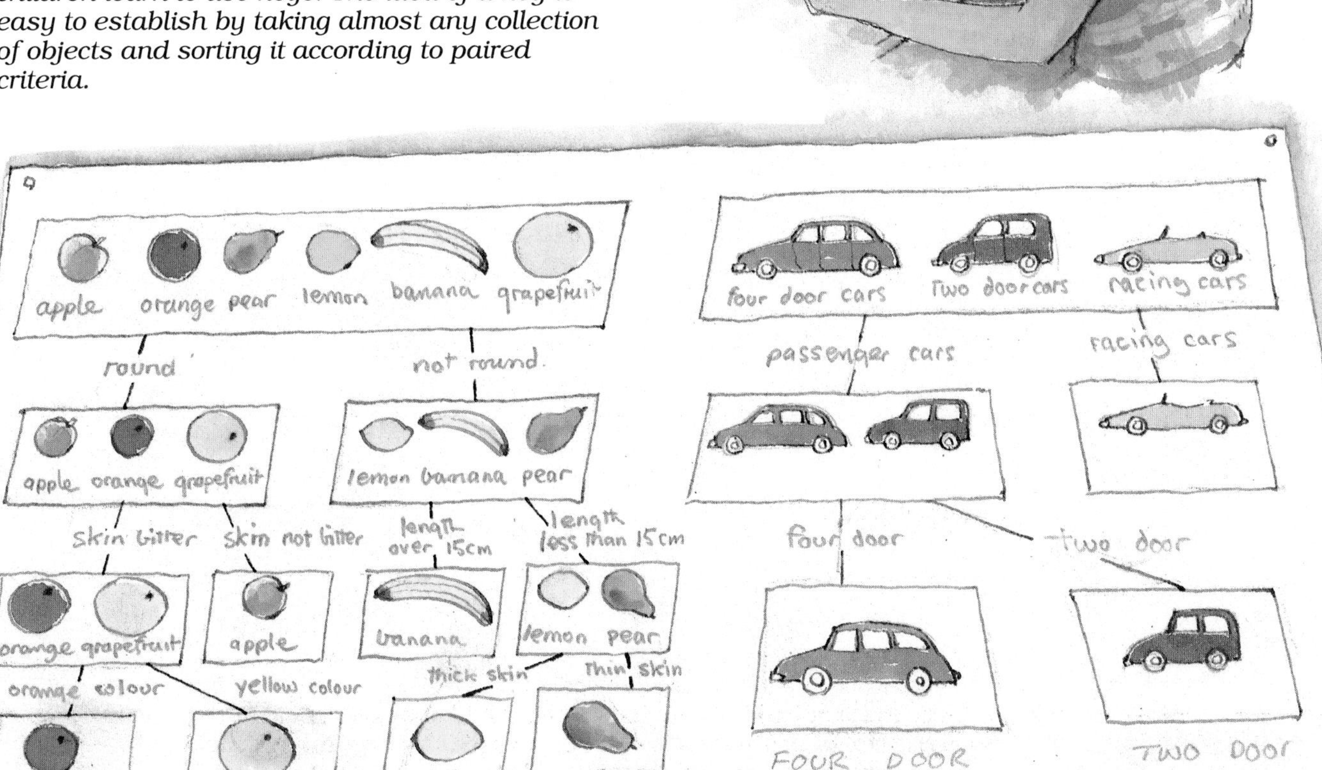

Further work

Surveying plants around the school is discussed in 'An Early Start to the Environment' (pages 10-11) and many investigations on plants are described in 'An Early Start to Nature'. Growing plants and gardening are to be found in 'An Early Start to Science', pages 14-17. 'An Early Start to Ourselves and Evolution', pages 46-51 has a section on life processes and plants.

Growing plants

Growing and caring for plants in the classroom and the immediate school environment, and thorough investigation of both cultivated and naturally growing plants, eventually begin to help children understand the diversity of plant life.

The ability to group plants into the major orders described on the preceding pages comes from such understanding. The references in the titles above give comprehensive coverage of this area of the National Curriculum Science Programme.

There are a number of computer programs dealing with keys.

Animals without backbones

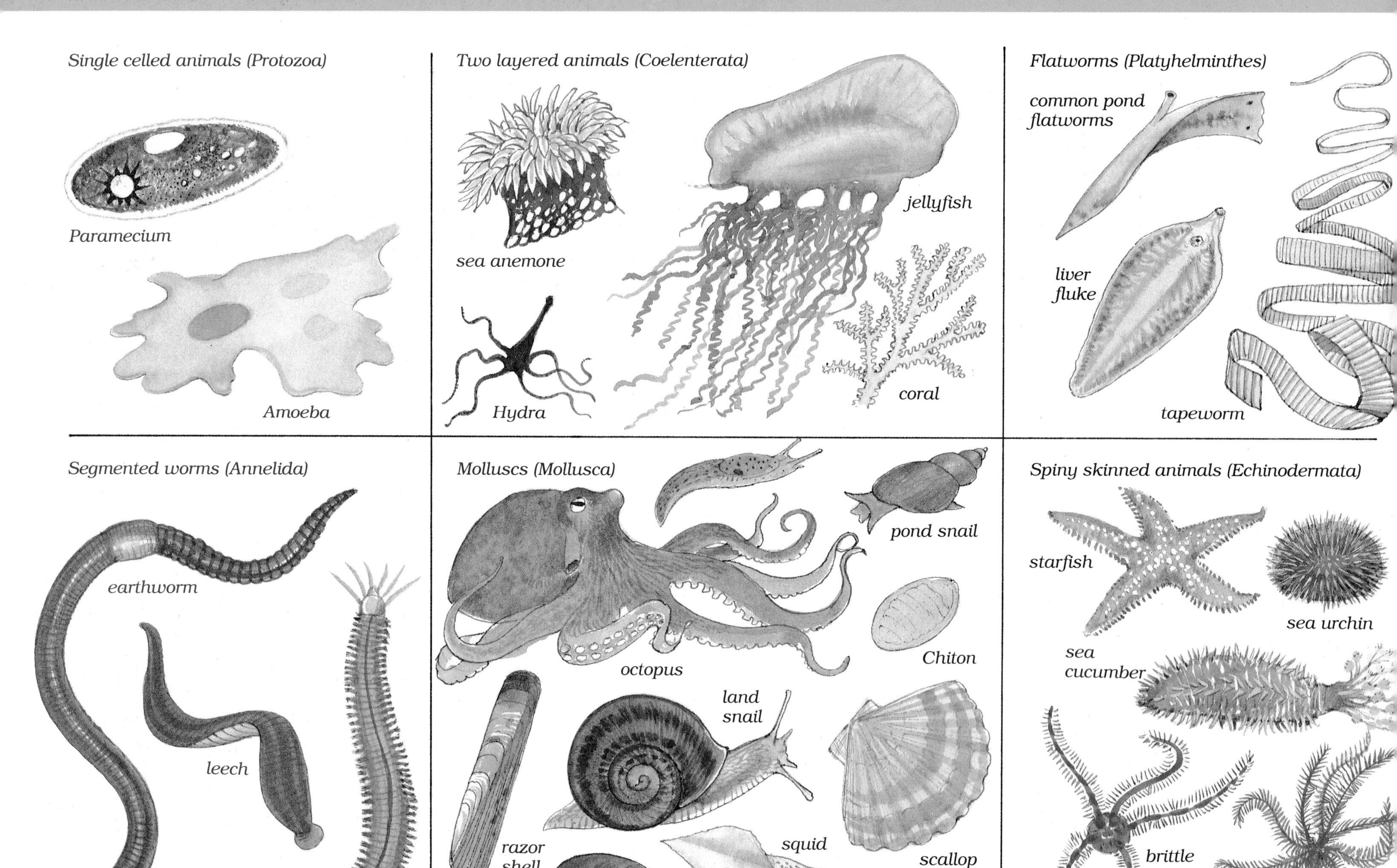

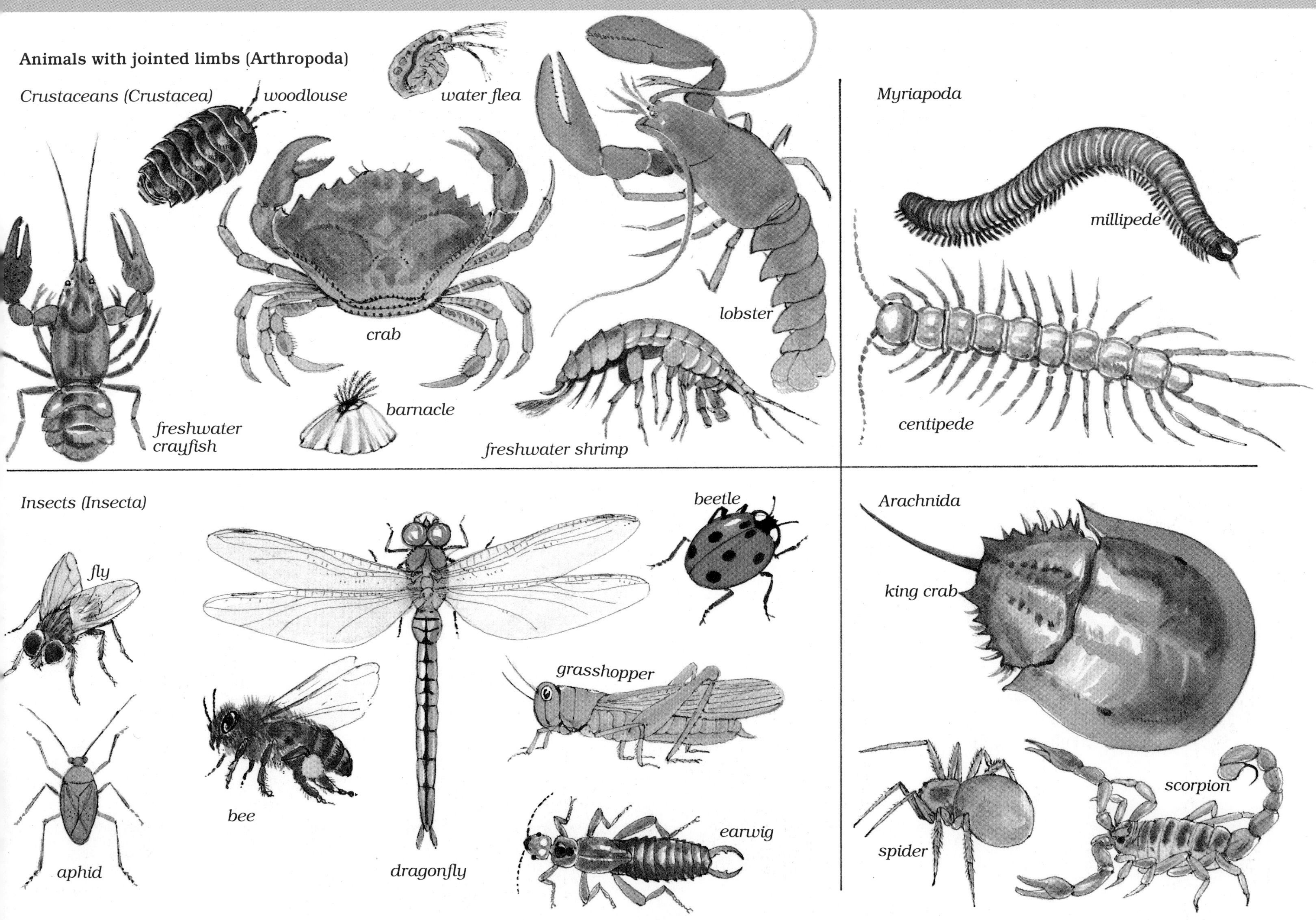
Animals with jointed limbs (Arthropoda)
Crustaceans (Crustacea)
woodlouse
water flea
crab
lobster
barnacle
freshwater crayfish
freshwater shrimp
Myriapoda
millipede
centipede
Insects (Insecta)
fly
aphid
bee
dragonfly
beetle
grasshopper
earwig
Arachnida
king crab
spider
scorpion

Animals with backbones

Mammals (Mammalia)
Monotremes (Monotremata)
spiny anteater
duckbilled platypus
Even toed ungulates (Artiodactyla)
deer
cow
giraffe
Insectivores (Insectivora)
hedgehog
mole
shrew
Rodents (Rodentia)
squirrel
mouse
rat
guinea pig
Primates
human
chimpanzee
lemur
baboon
Odd toed ungulates (Perissodactyla)
horse
tapir
rhinoceros
Lagomorphs (Lagomorpha)
hare
rabbit
Subungulata
hyrax
elephant
Bats (Chiroptera)
pipistrelle bat
fruit bat
Marsupials (Metatheria)
kangaroo
koala bear
opossum
Carnivores (Carnivora)
seal
tiger
stoat
dog
Cetacea
porpoise
whale
dolphin

Most animal groups that children come across are listed here but there are others, e.g. Sponges (Porifera), Threadworms (Nematoda), Wheel animals (Rotifera), Sea mats (Polyzoa), Lamp shells (Brachiopoda).

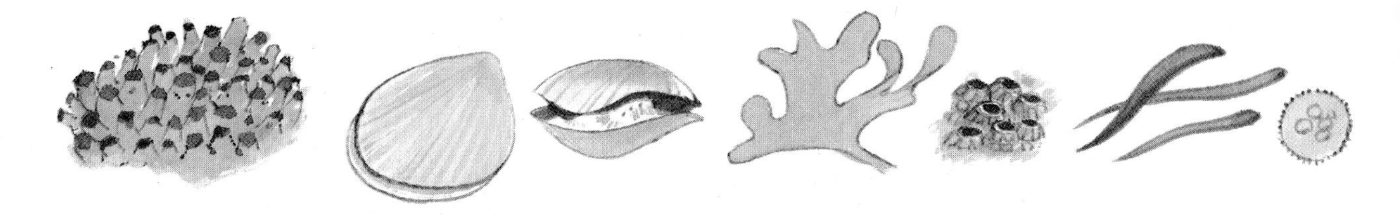

ANIMALS WITHOUT BACKBONES – INVERTEBRATES

Single celled animals – Protozoa
Microscopic. Structurally very simple and very abundant. All are found in water. *Amoeba*, *Paramecium*, *Euglena*.

Two layered animals – Coelenterata
Sack-like animals with the opening to the sac being the mouth. Most live in the sea. *Hydra*, jellyfish, sea anemones, corals.

Flatworms – Platyhelminthes
Small, flattened, unsegmented worms with no body cavity. Some are freshwater animals often found under stones and floating leaves. Many are parasitic. Pond flatworms, tapeworms, liver flukes.

Segmented worms – Annelida
These are true worms. They have a body cavity, a mouth and an anus. Included are the earthworms, many worms that live in ponds, and the lugworms, ragworms and bristleworms found on sandy shores.

Molluscs – Mollusca
These are soft bodied, unsegmented animals that usually have one or more calcareous shells. Snails, slugs, limpets, oysters, mussels, squid, octopus.

Spiny skinned animals – Echinodemata
Marine, unsegmented animals with the parts of the body showing a radial symmetry, usually along 5 radii. Starfish, brittle stars, sea urchins, sea cucumbers.

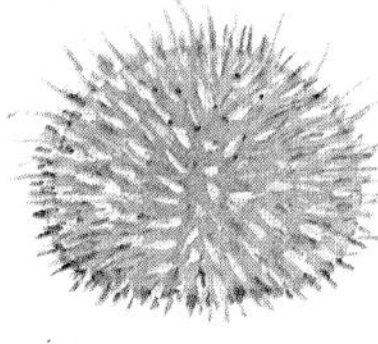

ANIMALS WITH JOINTED LIMBS – ARTHROPODA

Crustaceans – Crustacea
Mainly aquatic animals with two pairs of antennae and lots of paired limbs that are used for feeding, walking, swimming and breathing. Crabs, crayfish, shrimps, barnacles, water fleas, woodlice.

Insects

Insecta
Body divided into abdomen, thorax and head. The thorax has 6 legs, and usually bears wings. One of the most successful and prolific of all animal groups. Moths, butterflies, bees, wasps, ants, locusts, mosquitoes, dragonflies, flies, grasshoppers, cockroaches, earwigs, beetles, lice, termites.

Myriapoda
Animals with lots of segments each bearing similar legs. Centipedes are carnivorous with one pair of legs per segment. Millipedes are herbivorous with two pairs of legs per segment.

Arachnida
Body in two parts with four pairs of legs on the anterior part. Spiders, mites, scorpions, king crabs, ticks.

ANIMALS WITH BACKBONES – VERTEBRATES

Fishes – Pisces
Aquatic, move by means of a muscular tail and fins. Breathe through gills. Body of many covered in scales. Salmon, roach, stickleback, pike, herring, plaice, shark.

Amphibians – Amphibia
Partially adapted to life on land but eggs must be laid in water. Moist, shiny skin. Frogs, toads, newts, salamanders.

Reptiles – Reptilia
Completely adapted to life on land. Scaly bodies. Eggs protected by a shell and can be laid on land. Snakes, lizards, crocodiles, turtles, tortoises.

Birds – Aves
Characterized by feathers. Warm blooded. Specialized for flight. No teeth. Sparrows, ducks, penguins, owls, gulls, finches, robins.

Mammals – Mammalia
Hairy, warm-blooded animals. Young fed on milk produced by mammary glands. Duckbilled platypus, spiny anteater, kangaroo, opossum, Tasmanian devil, wombat, phalanger, man, lemur, loris, monkey, baboon, mandrill, gibbon, chimpanzee, orangutan, gorilla, shrew, mole, hedgehog, mouse, squirrel, beaver, lion, tiger, puma, mongoose, wolf, weasel, raccoon, panda, polar bear, sealion, walrus, seal, buffalo, goat, giraffe, elk, camel, pig, hippo, zebra, rhinoceros, tapir, hyrax, elephant, dolphin, porpoise, whale, bat.

Simpler classifications

There are many ways to classify animals. The classification of animals outlined on the preceding pages is a standard classification. Often, for children, their own simple classification made up from readily observable features may be the best to begin with.

Good work with animals can be done with the invertebrate life found around the school. It makes a good starting point for sorting and separating. 'An Early Start to the Environment', pages 6-9, has a classification which is based on sorting and separating animals without backbones according to their number of legs.

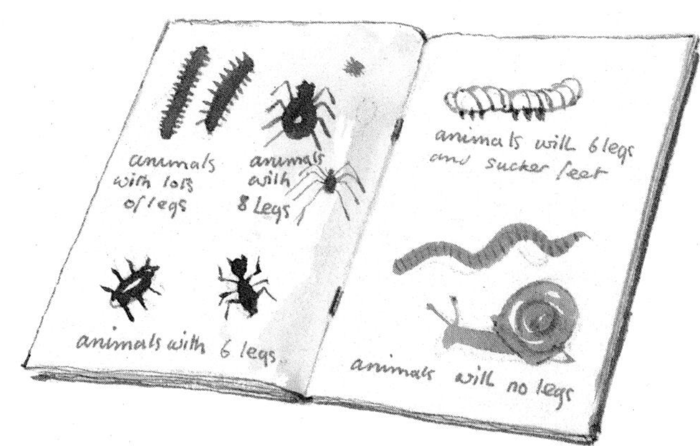

Collecting

Ways of collecting invertebrate animals from around the school are described in 'An Early Start to the Environment', page 5. Housing them and conducting investigations are to be found in 'An Early Start to Nature', pages 36-47. This latter book also describes activities that can be carried out with fish, amphibians and birds. 'An Early Start to Ourselves and Evolution' looks at life processes.

Mammals

Mice, guinea pigs, rats, rabbits, gerbils, hamsters and other mammals are often kept by children or housed in schools. Children are familiar with cats and dogs, and they come across the occasional wild animal such as a hedgehog, mole or badger – they can, of course, study themselves. There is much that can be done.

What to study in an animal

Personal facts
- *Common name. Scientific name.*
- *Sex. Stage in life history (if appropriate).*
- *Natural habitat.*

Appearance
- *Size. Shape. Texture. Colour.*

Make coloured drawings to show these. Add a scale.

Behaviour
- *How it moves. What it uses to help it move.*
- *How it feeds. What it feeds on.*
- *How it breathes. What it breathes through.*
- *How it responds to stimuli: Can it see? Does it respond to touch? Does it smell things? Does it like warmth? Does it prefer damp places? Does it like the dark?*
- *How it reproduces: Does it produce eggs? How many eggs? Does it look after its young? Is there a life cycle? Record its life history.*
- *How it gets rid of waste matter. Are there any droppings?*

Habit
- *Is it a solitary animal or does it live in groups?*
- *Is it a territorial animal?*
- *Does it have enemies?*
- *Does it affect its surroundings?*

Effects on people
- *Is it a 'harmful' animal? Is it a 'helpful' animal?*
- *Does it have to be controlled? How is this done?*

Grouping
- *Can children place it in its group?*

The atmosphere is the envelope of gases surrounding the Earth. Its chemical composition is fairly constant, but successive layers of the atmosphere display variations in properties. The main layers starting from ground level are the troposphere, the stratosphere and the ionosphere.

Troposphere

Air pressure and temperature decrease steadily as one moves upward. Winds, dust and water vapour are present. Between this layer and the next is a thin transitional layer called the tropopause. This varies in height with the latitude, season and weather. The tropopause marks the level at which temperature becomes constant, even with increasing height, for the next 50 miles (80 km). All weather occurs in the troposphere.

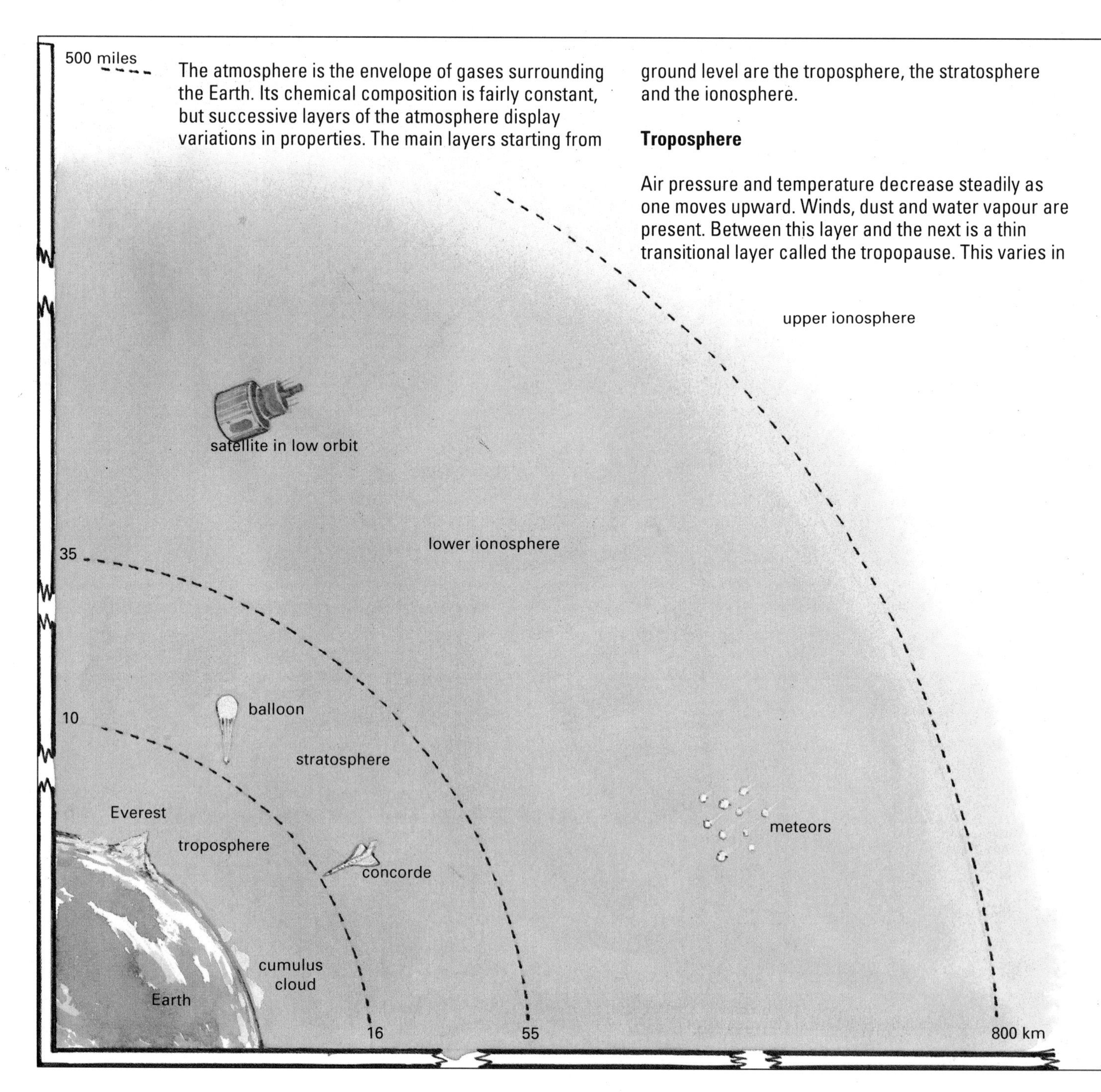

Stratosphere

This layer contains a thin ozone rich region just above the tropopause. The lower stratosphere is ideal for flying. Water vapour and dust are absent. Pressure decreases as you move upward through the stratosphere, but temperature remains constant.

Ionosphere

Pressure decreases up to about 56 miles (90 km) above the Earth and then remains almost constant to the very edge of the atmosphere. From this height temperature increases upward. Water vapour and dust are absent. There are several electrically conducting layers in the ionosphere; for example the aurora borealis is often seen in the lower ionosphere. The ionosphere also reflects radio waves around the world.

Functions of the atmosphere

As an insulator
The atmosphere acts as an insulating blanket. It stops temperatures in middle and high latitudes dropping to extremes during the night or during winter.

As a filter
The atmosphere protects us from those of the Sun's rays that are harmful. There is a thin layer of ozone in the stratosphere which prevents harmful rays from entering the atmosphere near the Earth. If this ozone layer is destroyed, life on Earth will cease.

As an agent for the water cycle
Evaporation from the oceans produces water vapour, which condenses into clouds in the atmosphere and falls as rain or snow.

Air is invisible. Its existence needs to be made real to children.

Catching air

Ask a child to take a plastic bag and scoop up some air.

Screw up the neck of the bag.

Keep a tight hold on the neck of the bag and squeeze it with the other hand.

The push of air

Try pouring some water into a funnel firmly sealed into the neck of a bottle.

Use a bottle with a narrow neck. A clear glass wine bottle is ideal.

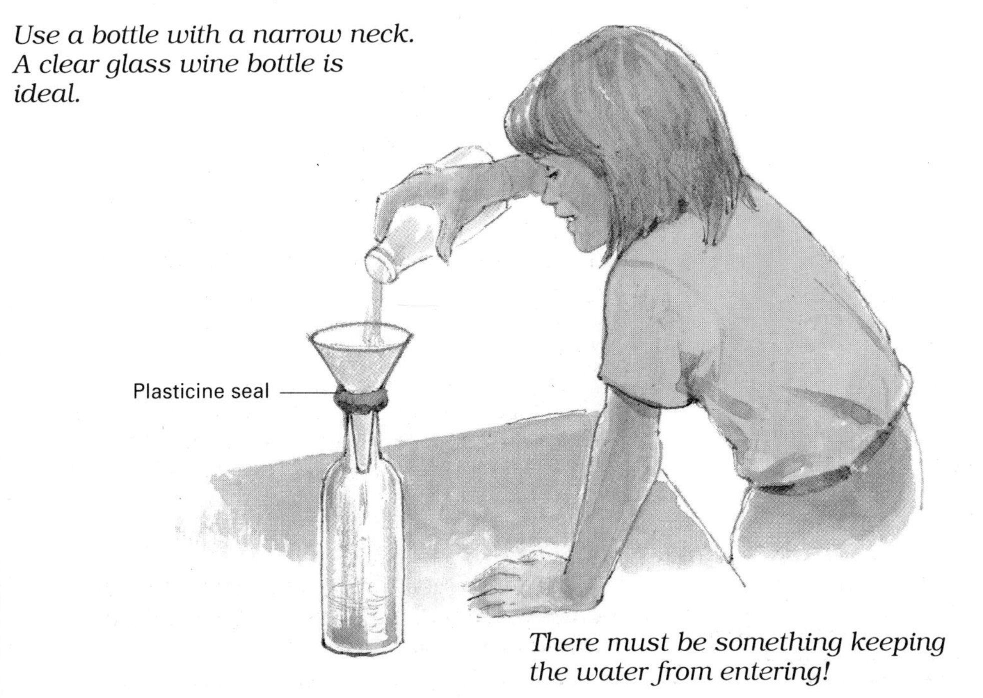

There must be something keeping the water from entering!

Shifting air

Put a bottle into a bucket of water and let it fill up with water.

Hold it in the water so that it can receive bubbles of air from a second bottle plunged into the bucket.

Air resistance

Let a child run with a large piece of card held in front – the side from a large supermarket carton is a good thing to use. The child will be able to 'feel' the air.

It's easy! Or is it?

Place a dried pea in the neck of a bottle which is laid on its side.

Can the children blow it in?

Despite appearances air has weight and it exerts a pressure. There is a lot of air in the atmosphere and it exerts a lot of pressure. In reality it squeezes all around us. Here are some things to show this effect.

Air can squeeze

Suck the air out of a clean, thin-sided plastic container.

What happens?

Air can hold

Push a sink plunger on to a smooth clean surface.

What holds it on?

Damp the edges of two sink plungers and press them together.

Try to pull them apart.

Why is it hard to do so?

Air can break

Place an old worn ruler on a table with half its length projecting over the edge.

Spread a newspaper over the table and over the part of the ruler on the table.

Smooth the newspaper so that all the air is removed from beneath it.

Give the ruler a sharp blow.

It usually breaks sharply, illustrating the air pressure over the large area of the newspaper.

A thin ruler and practice make for a dramatic demonstration.

Air can glue

Wet two plastic rulers, press them flat sides together.

Try to separate them without sliding them apart.

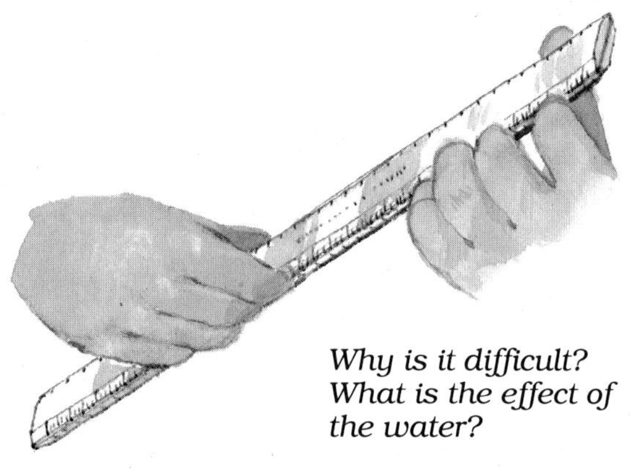

Why is it difficult? What is the effect of the water?

Two pieces of glass are even better!

Moving air

Place two identical books side by side with a gap between them.

Put a sheet of paper over the gap.

Blow down the tunnel.

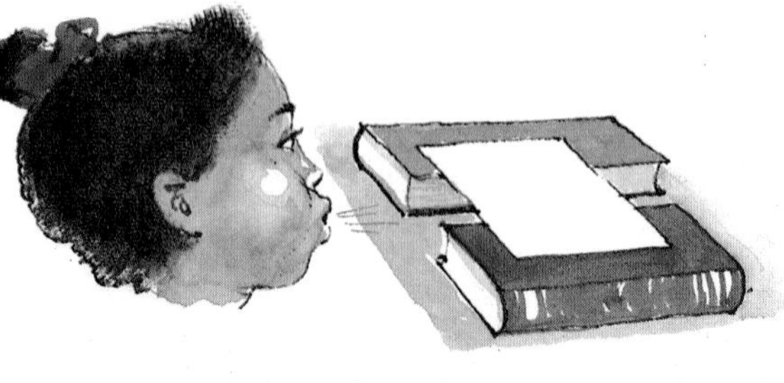

Does the sheet blow away?

How does the bird fountain on the budgerigar cage work?

Can you blow them away?

Hang two tin cans or two table tennis balls about 2 cm apart.

Blow between them.

What happens?

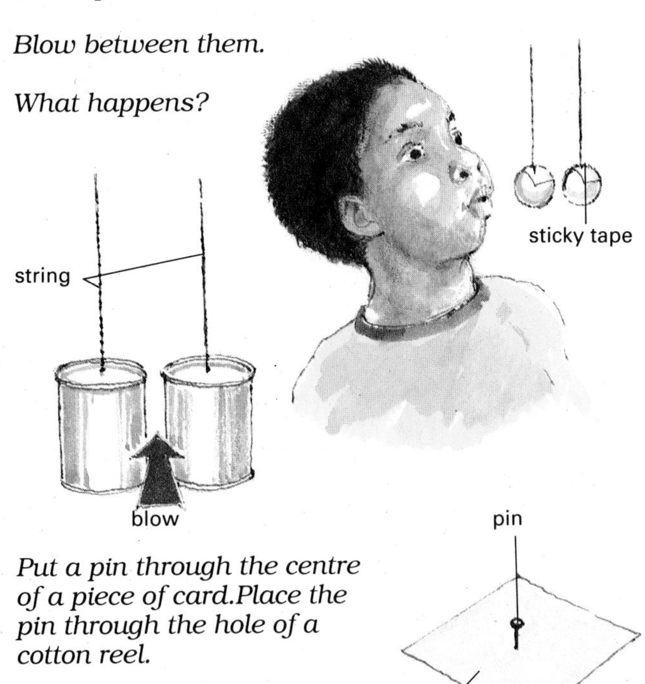

Put a pin through the centre of a piece of card.Place the pin through the hole of a cotton reel.

Blow through the other end.

Can you blow the card away?

pin
card
blow
pin
card

Water and air pressure

Some of these tests are messy, but they are fun. Do them over a sink.

Fill a tumbler to the brim with water. Slide a piece of card over the top.

Hold the card with one hand and invert the tumbler.

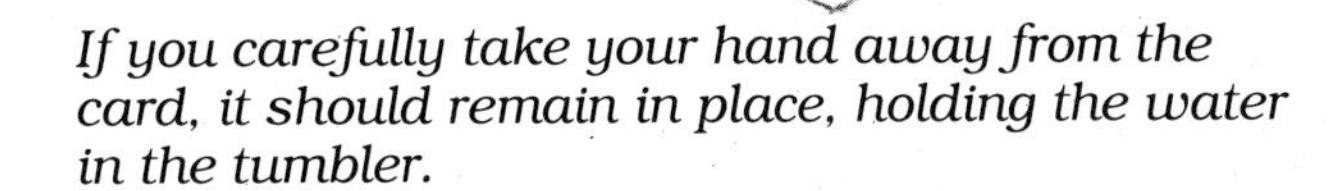

If you carefully take your hand away from the card, it should remain in place, holding the water in the tumbler.

What is pressing on the card to hold the water in? Does it work if the tumbler is half full?

> The water pressure is pushing the card down, but the air pressure pushes it up. It is enough to stop the card and the water from falling.

Screw a handkerchief into a ball and put it in the base of a jam jar.

Invert the jam jar and push it, mouth downward, into a bucket of water.

Take it out again.

Is it wet or dry?

Take a medicine dropper and fill it with water.

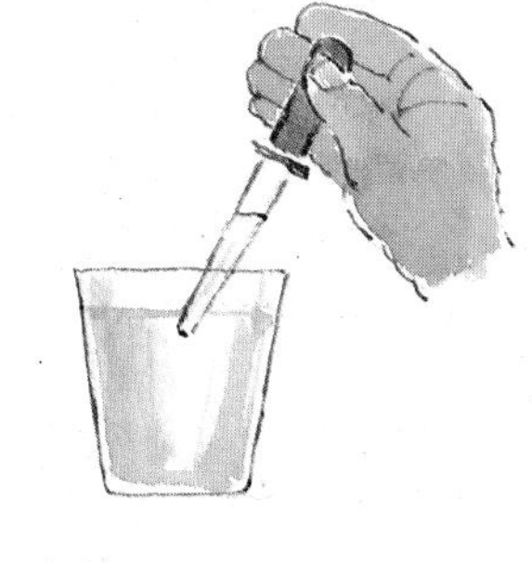

How does it work?

Fountain pens working on a sac principle are becoming popular again. These also work like the medicine dropper.

Take a tin can with a press-on lid.

Make one hole in the centre of the lid, and several holes in the base.

Fill it with water iat a sink.

Keep a finger over the hole in the lid and lift the tin up.

What happens?

Take your finger off the hole.

What happens?

Relate this to the need to make two holes in a condensed milk can in order to get the contents out.

Evangelista Torricelli

The history of the discovery that air presses on us is an interesting one. Very shortly before he died in 1642 Galileo invited a young mathematician, Evangelista Torricelli, to come and work with him in Florence. On Galileo's death Torricelli became Philosopher and Mathematician to the Duke of Florence.

Torricelli had been experimenting with a long tube fixed to the side of a building in order to find out about the column of water it would hold and the vacuum left in the tube above the water. This was cumbersome, so he hit upon the idea of using mercury, a liquid metal. Its density meant that he could use a much shorter tube.

Torricelli believed, and was proved right, that the air pressing down on the surface of the mercury in the dish would hold a column of mercury. He thus invented the mercury barometer.

A mercury barometer is a tube sealed at the top so that no air can enter. Above the mercury in the tube is a vacuum. The mercury in the tube pushes down but is held up by the air pressure pushing on the mercury in the dish.

The height of the mercury is read from the surface of the mercury in the dish to the level in the tube. At normal air pressure this is about 760mm.

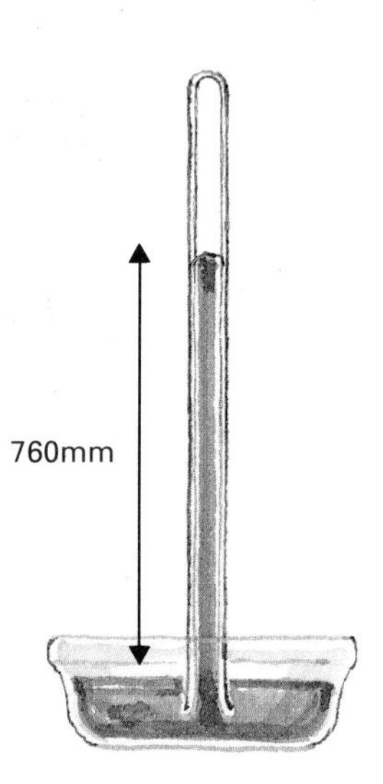

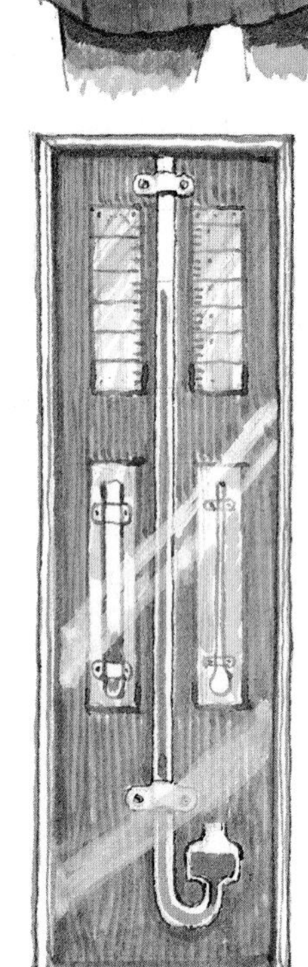

Mercury barometers are still used today. However, they are not easy to carry around and are usually fixed to one site. The aneroid ('dry') barometer is easier to carry.

In such a barometer, air has been partly evacuated from a sealed circular box. If the air pressure increases slightly it pushes harder on this box. A set of levers fixed to the box causes a pointer to move over a scale.

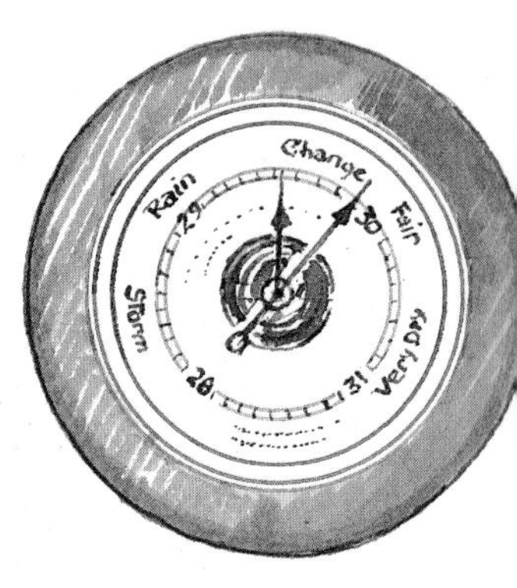

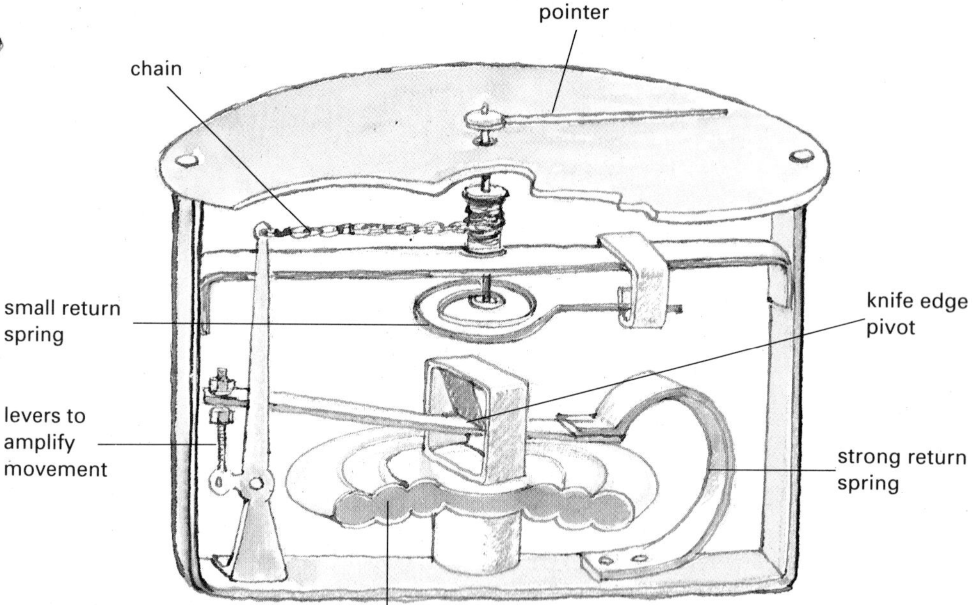

Bicycle pump

A common tool used by children that depends on air pressure to work it is the bicycle pump.

Pulling the handle back allows air into the lower region of the pump. Pushing the handle forward flexes the washer against the sides of the pump and thus forces the air outward.

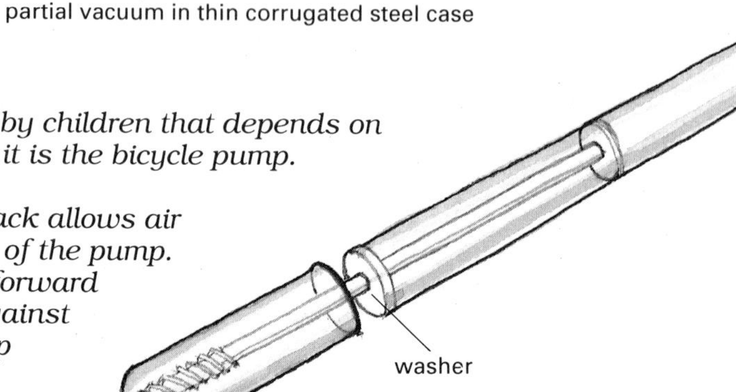

Blaise Pascal

Torricelli's discovery became known to a Frenchman, Blaise Pascal, who thought up some experiments he wanted to try. Because he was unwell, and because he needed someone to climb a mountain, he got his brother-in-law, a Monsieur Perier, to do the experiments for him.

On the morning of 19 September 1648, two clergymen, two lawyers and a doctor gathered in a monastery at the foot of a mountain, the Puy-de-Dôme in France. Perier set up two mercury barometers and recorded the height of the mercury in each. It was exactly the same in each tube. He left one tube with the monks to keep a record of its height through the day and took the other up the mountain together with his five observers.

At the top of the mountain, which was about 1500 m high, he set up his barometer again. The column of mercury was now 6cm shorter than before. Back at the monastery the control barometer had not changed throughout the day.

The thinner air at the top of the mountain had held up a shorter column of mercury – that is, air pressure decreases with altitude.

Otto Guericke

Otto Guericke was mayor of the German city of Magdeburg. He was interested in making air pumps and experimented until he had made a very efficient one.

To test it he had two cast-iron hemispheres made which fitted together well. Using his pump, he extracted the air from inside the sphere and then had two teams of eight horses hitched, one to each hemisphere. Pull as they might, they could not separate the hemispheres against the outside pressure of the air. Page 40 shows how to simulate this using sink plungers.

Air pressure and flight

The forces operating on an aeroplane in flight are discussed in 'An Early Start to Technology', page 50. Here we are looking at the force that causes lift in greater detail, for it is tied up with air pressure.

Do the following experiments with children.

Moving air past things

Hold two strips of paper a short distance apart and blow between them.

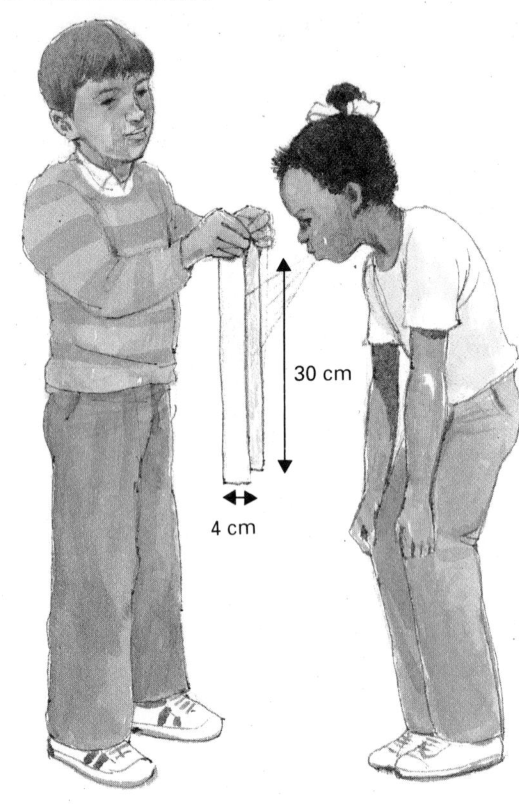

Children expect them to fly apart, but they come together.

The air pressure between them is reduced; the air pressure on the outside thus forces them in.

Ask a child to blow over the top of a sheet of paper.

The fast moving air over the top of the sheet reduces the pressure. The air pressure underneath the sheet therefore forces the paper upward

Wind on wings

Take a sheet of A4 paper and fold it in half. Curve and glue the top half to the bottom half to form an aerofoil shape.

Make a hole through both sheets. Insert a length of drinking straw, positioning it between the two holes.

Thread a piece of cotton through the straw.

Blow against the front, and then against the rear, of the wing. What happens?

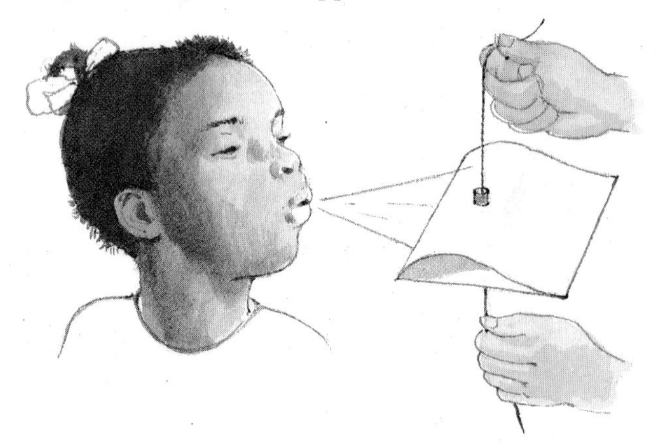

Moving things through air

Try running with a stiff piece of card held at an angle.

Change the angle. Run again.

Curve the front edge. Run again.

Can you feel lift?
Can you feel drag?

This principle of faster moving air causing a reduced pressure is used in an aircraft wing.

The air moving over the longer top surface of the wing has to move faster. The slower moving air underneath the wing presses more, and so the wing lifts.

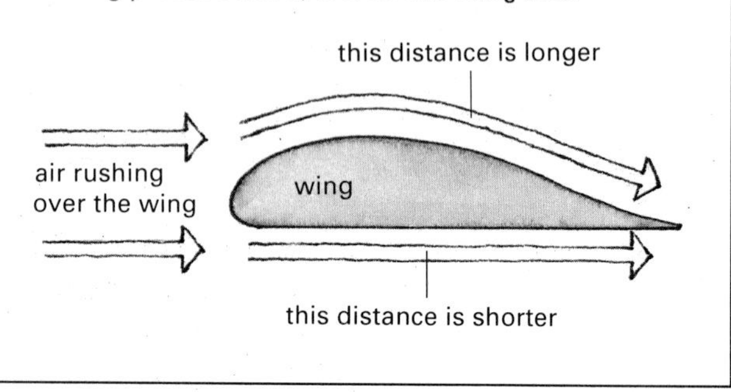

A paper glider

There are various aircraft and other flying things to investigate in 'An Early Start to Technology', pages 50-57. Here is another aircraft to make. It moves beautifully on the air.

1 *Take a sheet of A4 paper.*

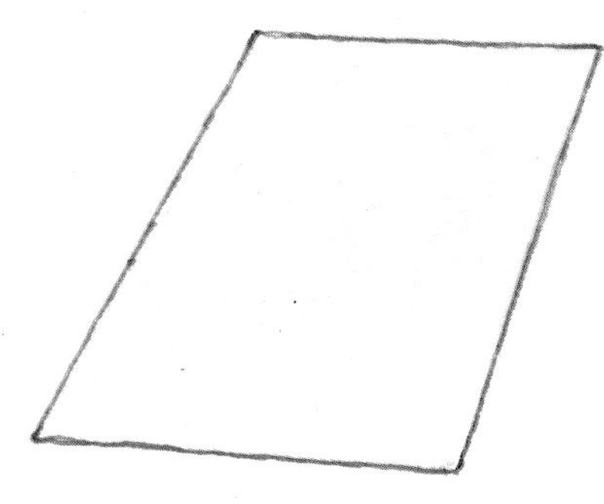

2 *Fold the two top corners to the centre.*

3 *Fold the triangle that has been formed to the centre.*

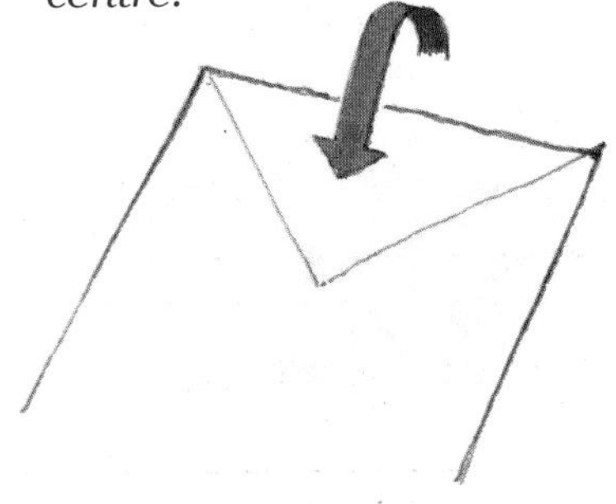

4 *Fold in each corner.*

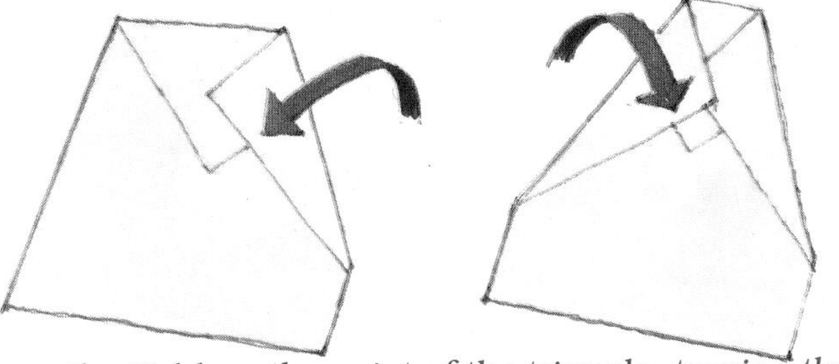

5 *Fold up the point of the triangle, tearing the paper slightly on both sides.*

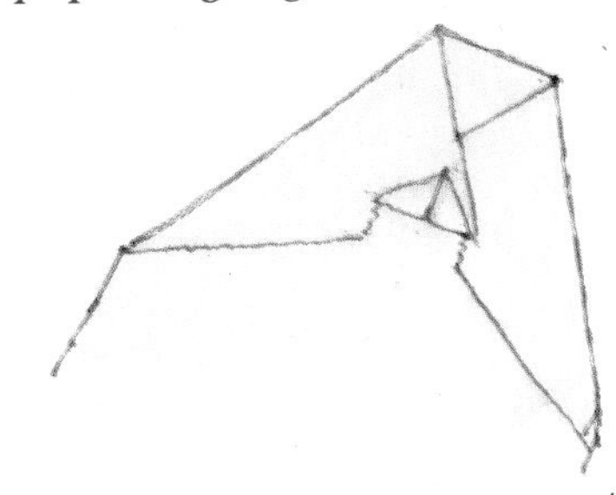

6 *Fold up along the centre line.*

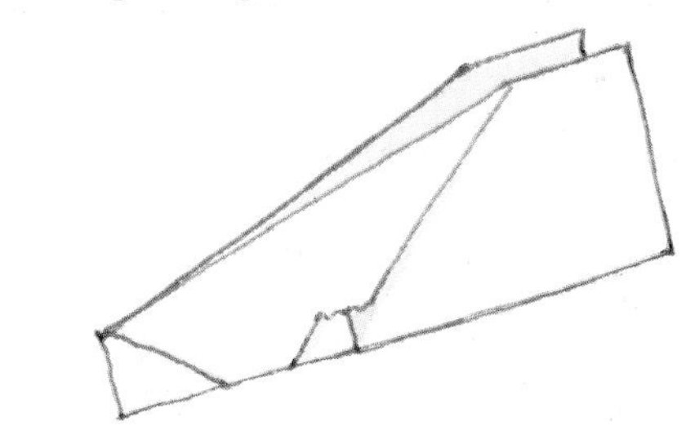

7 *Fold down the wings.*

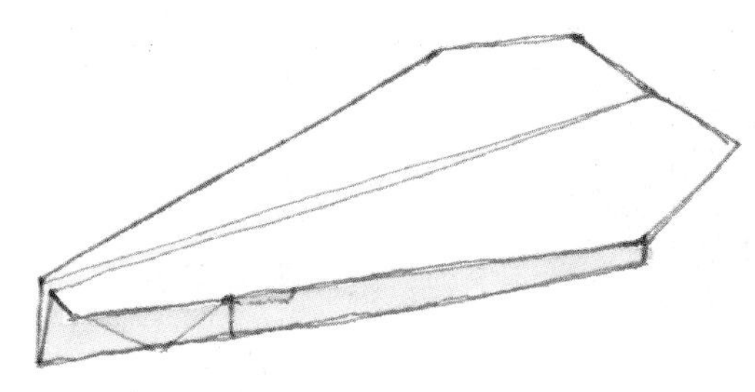

8 *Open out the wings – they must not be too tightly folded.*

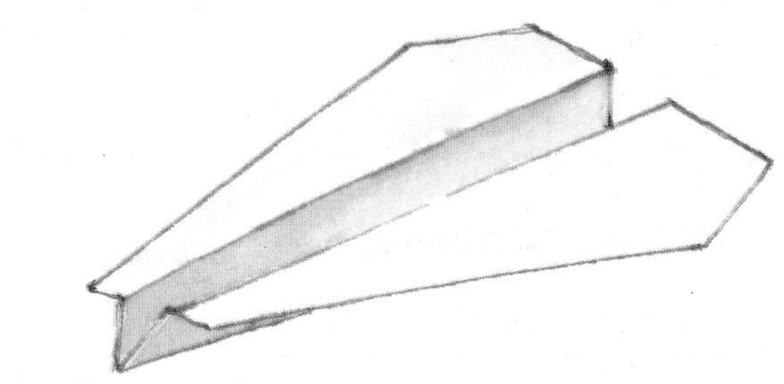

9 *Test fly your plane.*

10 *Adjust the wingtips to turn right, turn left or loop the loop.*

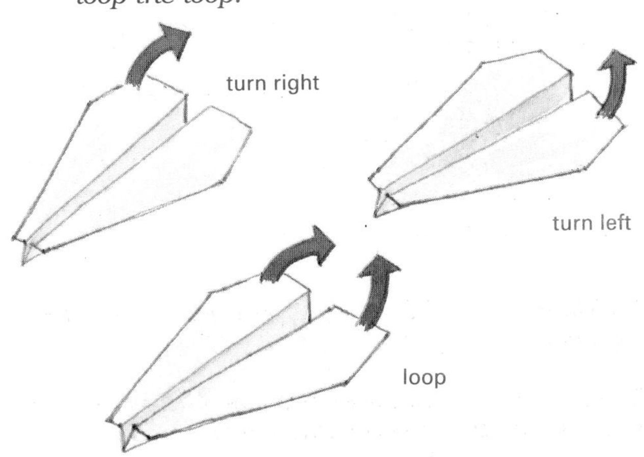

The amount of water vapour in the atmosphere varies. If we take dry air the volume composition is
- 78% nitrogen
- 21% oxygen
- 1% argon, with minute traces of neon, helium, krypton and xenon, and about 0.03% carbon dioxide.

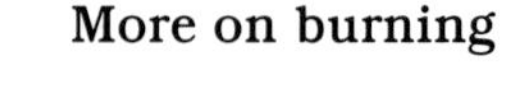

Burning

Put a candle stub on a tin lid and float it on a little water in a large Pyrex bowl.

Light the candle. Invert a jar with a wide neck over it.

As the candle burns it uses up the oxygen in the air. The water rises to replace the oxygen that has been used.

Rusting

Rusting uses up part of the air.

Jam some steel wool into the bottom of a jam jar. Invert it over a little water in a bowl. Mark the level of the water in the jar.

Put it on a windowsill out of the way and leave it for some days.

What happens to the water level?

More on burning

The part of the air that supports combustion is oxygen.

Take three different sized glass jars with smooth rims. Grease each rim with Vaseline or lard. Keep them ready for inversion over birthday candles.

Arrange three birthday candles on a smooth surface – glass is ideal but a smooth plastic tray may do. Melt the base of each candle slightly to make it stick.

Light the candles.

Place the jars over the candles all at the same time.

How long does each candle burn?

How does the volume of the jar compare with the length of time that the candle burns?

Jar	Volume	Time candle burns
1		
2		
3		

It is often stated in experiments with burning a candle in a jar that 'one-fifth of the air is used up' or that 'the lighted candle goes out because it has used up all the oxygen'. Under experimental conditions that is rarely, if ever, so. The lighted candle heats the air in the jar, causing it to expand. Some air is pushed out under the bottom of the jar, and this air cannot get back in when the jar cools. In reality the candle uses about one-third of the available oxygen.

The greenhouse effect

The amount of carbon dioxide in the air has been increasing over the last 100 years. Why?

Industry has increased.

Fossil fuels give off carbon dioxide when burnt.

Forests have been cut down.

Seas have been polluted.

Loss of trees and death of seaweeds and plankton cut back on the world's 'photosynthetic bank' – the stock of plants which use up carbon dioxide and release oxygen.

The carbon dioxide in the air acts as a blanket. Heat is prevented from escaping into space. This is called the greenhouse effect. The carbon dioxide has a similar effect to the glass in the greenhouse that traps the heat.

Extraction of natural gas, and farming, both cause the release of methane (natural gas is itself methane). This is an even more powerful greenhouse gas than carbon dioxide.

Collect accounts from newspapers about the greenhouse effect. Make your own record too.

Region	Effect
Polar caps	Getting warmer and melting. Sea levels could rise by 6m.
Europe	Getting warmer. Possible flooding. Special difficulties for countries like Holland.
North America	Getting warmer. Droughts affecting grain crops.

Damage to the ozone layer

The ozone rich layer just above the tropopause cuts down the amount of ultraviolet rays from the Sun that reach the ground. These are the rays that give us a suntan. They burn the skin. If the ozone layer is damaged too many of these rays could get through.

The use of CFCs (chlorofluorocarbons) in aerosol sprays, refrigerators, air conditioning units and the manufacture of expanded plastic foams, releases chemicals into the air. These pass up through the atmosphere and chemically react with the ozone. Thinning has begun to appear in the ozone layer. This means that more ultraviolet radiation can penetrate the Earth's atmosphere, causing sunburn, skin cancer and eye damage.

Design a poster to alert people to the danger of using CFCs.

Collect pictures of things that cause damage to the ozone layer. Make a wall display.

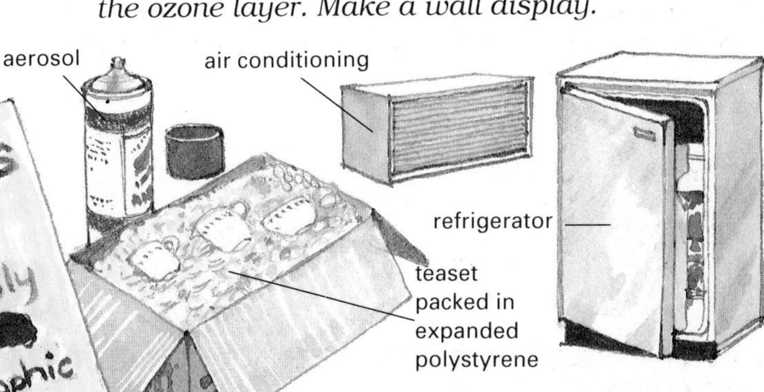

Discuss ways to get their production curbed or banned.

Acid rain

Pollutants from vehicles, factories and power stations combine with water in the air to make acid rain. The main pollutants are sulphur dioxide and nitrogen oxides. Sulphur dioxide combines with water to make weak sulphurous acid, and nitrogen oxide combines with water to make nitric acid. When they fall as rain, these acids, though weak, can cause immense damage to plant life, poison soils, build up in lakes, eat away at stonework and affect our health by being breathed in and taken in drinking water. The acids can be present in dust which settles on buildings and eats away at their exteriors. Prevailing winds carry such pollution from the United Kingdom to countries like Norway and Sweden, which create little air pollution of their own.

Make a frieze to illustrate the production and effects of acid rain.

Discuss possible ways of dealing with the problem of acid rain:
- *by reducing pollution*
- *by turning to other energy sources that don't produce pollutants, e.g. sun, wind and wave energy (see 'An Early Start to Energy', page 70)*
- *by liming acid lakes to neutralize the acid (a short term solution – see page 11 for the effects of adding lime).*

Make a display of alternative energy sources.

Pollen – a natural 'pollutant'?

Some children suffer from allergic reactions to pollen grains in the air. Flowering plants release pollen, which is carried from flower to flower by insects or transported by the wind. It is the windborne pollen that is of concern to sufferers from hay fever.

The plants mainly responsible for this are trees and grasses. Wind-pollinated trees tend to produce their pollen from late winter to the end of spring and, in general, are not of great consequence in causing hay fever. However, large numbers of hay-fever sufferers are sensitive to the pollen of grasses, which is produced during the period from June to August.

Much of this pollen is produced in country areas, but the wind often carries it into towns and cities. Hay fever is more of a problem than it used to be because the allergic symptoms are worsened by breathing polluted city air.

Relief is brought when weather conditions change as rain washes pollen out of the atmosphere.

Hay fever

Ask hay-fever sufferers to describe their symptoms and their treatment, e.g. sneezes, itchy eyes, runny or stuffy noses, sensitivity to sunlight; treatment by vaccines and antihistamines.

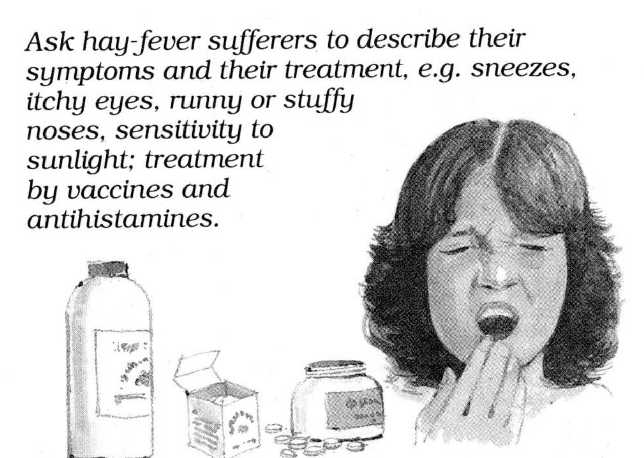

Temperature, humidity and the pollen count

The amount of pollen in the air varies with the temperature and humidity.

Daily temperature and humidity can be recorded, or taken from data published in the national press. The pollen count is also published daily as well as being announced on the radio and television.

Some of the grasses whose pollen can cause hay fever.

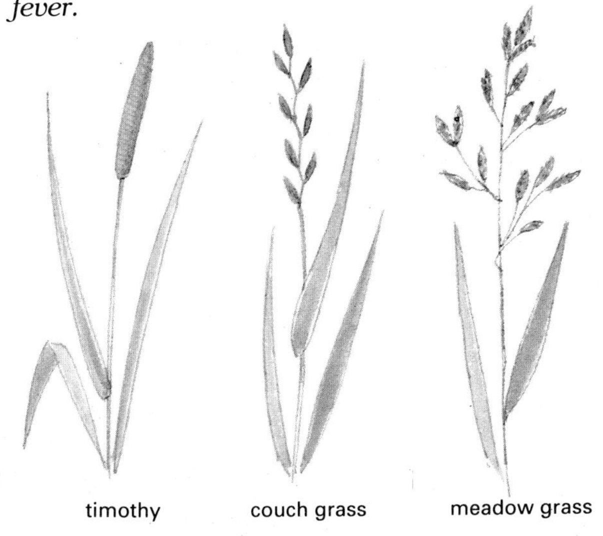

> **Pollen count**
>
> The pollen count is the number of grass pollen grains per cubic metre of air, averaged over 24 hours.

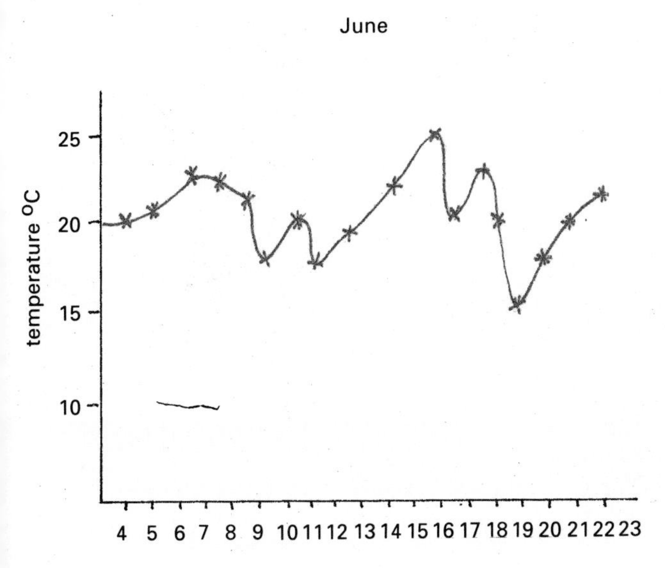

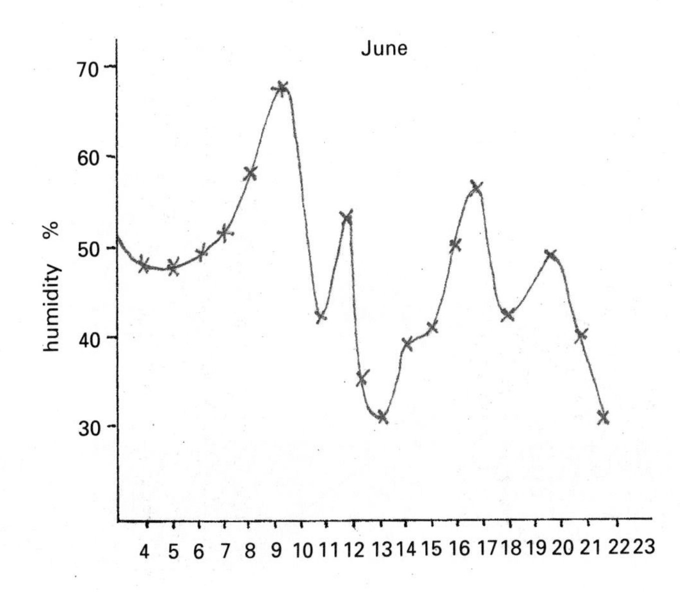

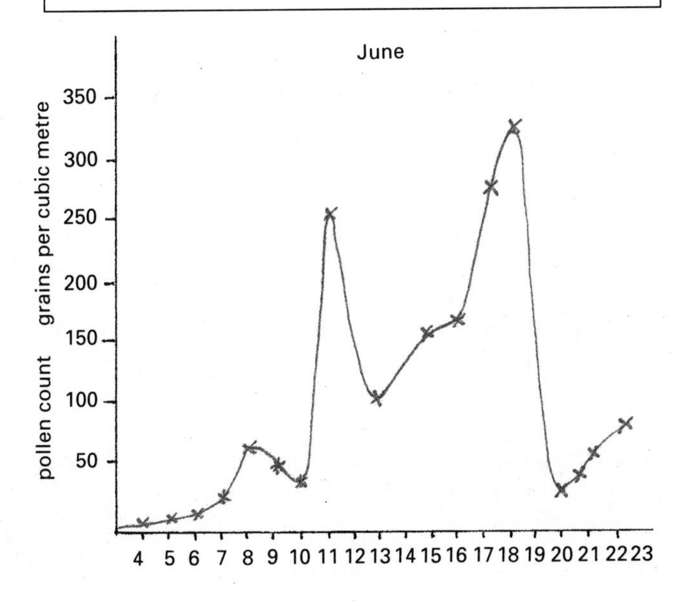

My Shadow

I have a little shadow that goes in and out
with me,
And what can be the use of him is more than
I can see,
He is very, very like me from the heels up to
the head;
And I see him jump before me, when I jump
into my bed.

The funniest thing about him is the way he
likes to grow
Not at all like proper children, which is
always very slow;
For he sometimes shoots up taller like an
india-rubber ball,
And he sometimes gets so little that there's
none of him at all.

He hasn't got a notion of how
children ought to play,
And can only make a fool of me
in every sort of way.
He stays so close beside me, he's
a coward you can see;
I'd think shame to stick to nursie as
that shadow sticks to me.

One morning, very early, before the
sun was up,
I rose and found the shining dew on
every buttercup.
But my lazy little shadow, like an
arrant sleepyhead,
Had stayed at home behind me and
was fast asleep in bed.

R.L. Stevenson

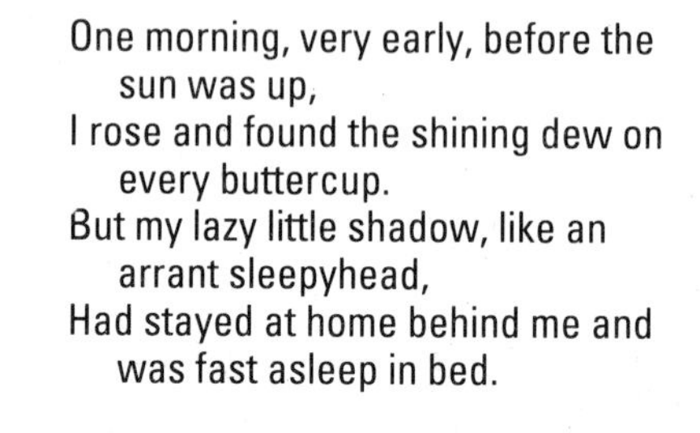

The rotation of the Earth

The rotation of the Earth is an abstract idea for children, and even though the concept is readily accepted by adults it still needs quite a lot of thought to marshal evidence to substantiate it.

One of the major pieces of contributing evidence is the apparent movement of the Sun across the sky. For children, plenty of experience with shadows helps develop this idea. Both 'An Early Start to Science' (pages 26-28) and 'An Early Start to Energy' (pages 15-17) offer a wealth of experiences to be gained from shadow play. From these experiences children will begin to appreciate that:

- *shadow length changes during the day*
- *shadows can be sharp or fuzzy, depending on the weather*
- *the angle at which light falls on a particular object will affect the shape of the shadow*
- *the Sun changes height in the sky through the year*

Tracking a shadow

The easiest way to show the Sun's movement using shadows is to chalk round a child's shoes first thing in the morning, thus making a permanent mark on the playground. The shadow cast can then be drawn.

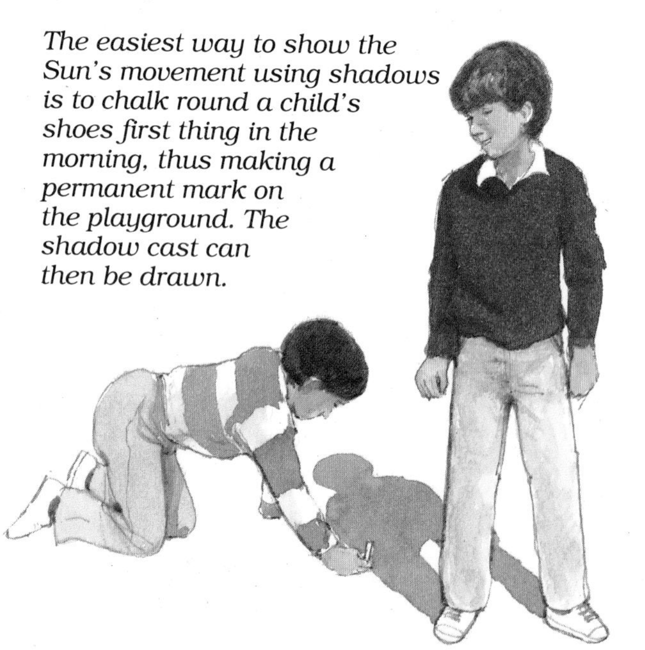

Return the same child to the chalk shoe marks through the day and draw the shadow cast.

Alternatively, use a broom handle tied to a box.

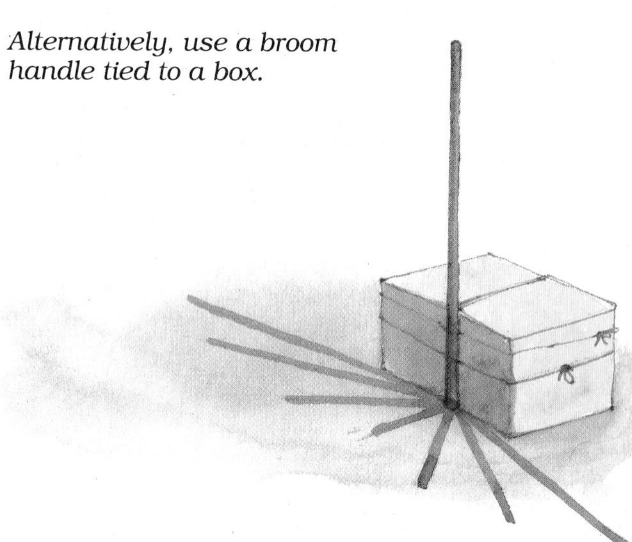

Discuss the movement of the shadow from west to east.
Try predicting where the shadow will be at various times of the day.

More work on shadows

The length of shadows cast by a stick through the day can easily be turned into a histogram. Here is one showing shadow length at 30 minute intervals between 9 am and 6 pm.

shadow length

9.00 10.00 11.00 12.00 13.00 14.00 15.00 16.00 17.00 18.00

time

Discuss how the shadows show the Sun's seeming movement from east to west. Tracing these shadows at two or three times through the year will also show how the Sun is higher in the sky at some times of the year.

Shadows cast in the classroom can be another way to illustrate the movement of the Sun.

Make a cross on the window with masking tape and chart the shadow cast down the wall by making crosses on mounted sheets of paper. Use a south-facing window.

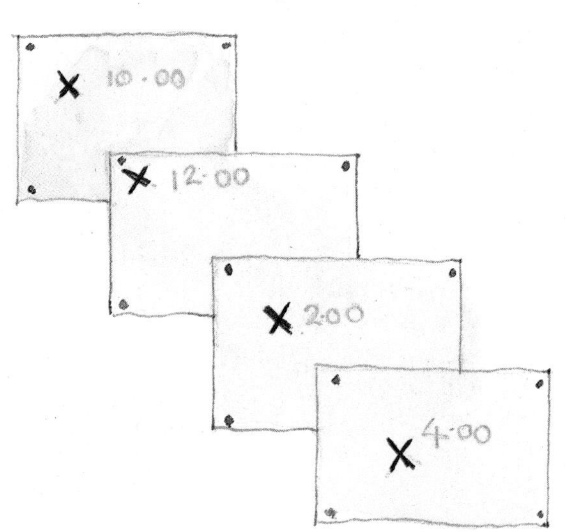

Alternatively, you could make chalk marks on an old table to trace the shadow cast by a window frame. Again use a south-facing window.

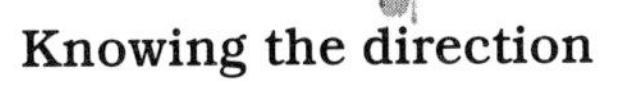

Knowing the direction

It is essential in this kind of work to establish the cardinal points of the compass. If children are unfamiliar with the positions of north, south, east and west they will need to be taught.

The apparent movement of the Sun across the sky acted as the principal timekeeper for people such as the ancient Egyptians, and persisted as the main means of telling the time well into the Middle Ages. The sundial, in many forms, predominated. Basically,it consists of a triangular central piece called the gnomon (from the Greek work for 'to know') which casts a shadow on a numbered scale of hours.

Setting up a sundial

In order for the shadow to move fairly uniformly over the face of the sundial the gnomon must be set parallel to the Earth's axis. At the North Pole the tip of the gnomon would point straight up to the North Star, since the Earth's axis points in that direction – that is to say, it would have an angle of 90°.

At London, because of the curvature of the Earth, the North Star appears lower in the sky and the tip of the gnomon must be adjusted to suit the latitude. Its angle here is 51.5°.

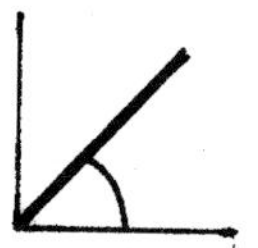

At the Equator, where the North Star is right on the horizon, the gnomon is horizontal, so that an ordinary horizontal dial cannot be used.

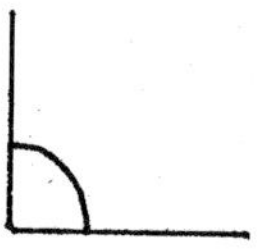

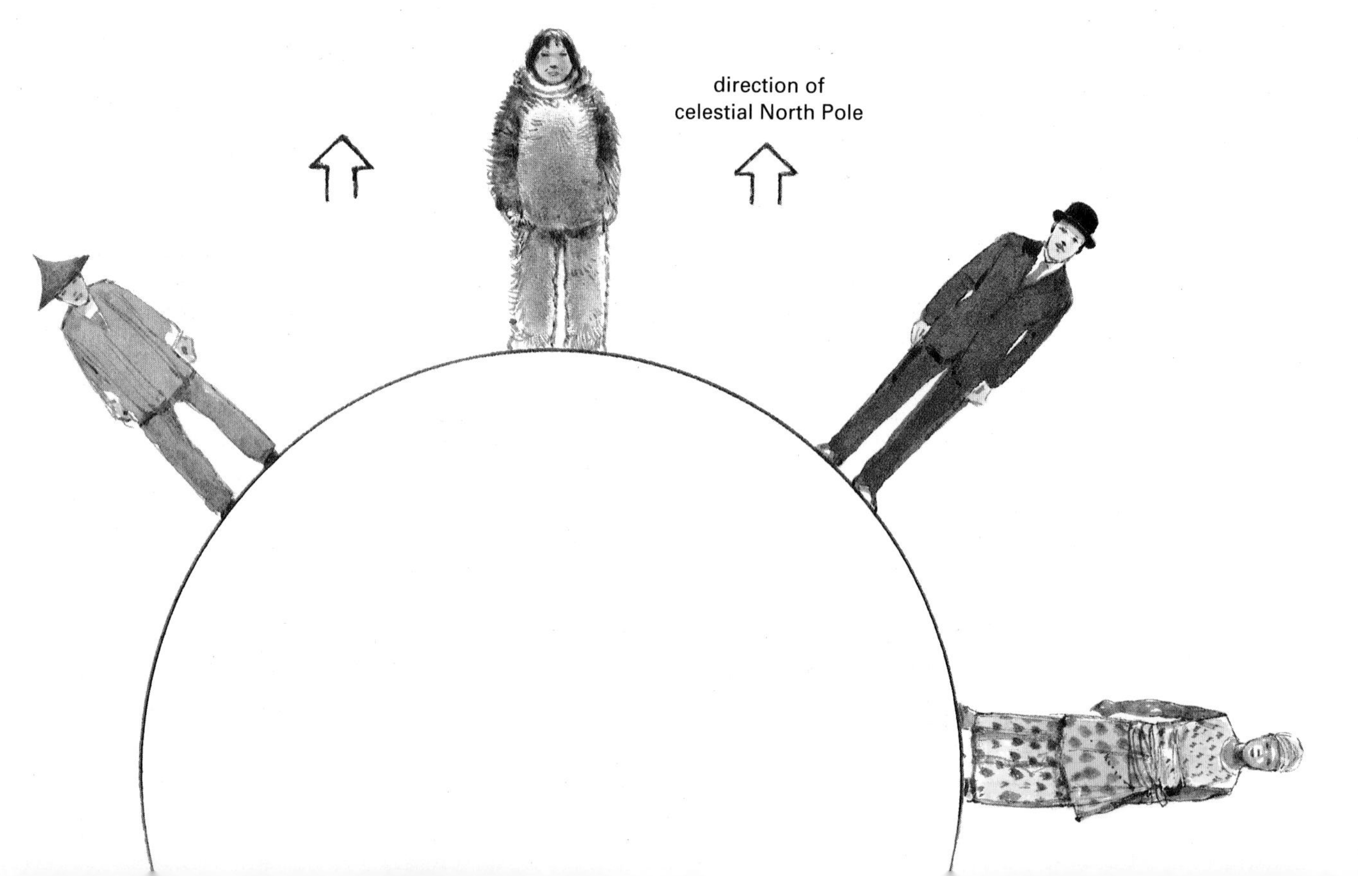

Because the shadow moves more slowly over the sundial at midday when the sun is overhead, you will find that the numbers are placed closer together towards noon, and farther apart towards morning and evening.

Children can make many kinds of sundial. Here are some suggestions.

Simple sundial

card gnomon

20 cm

51.5°

15 cm

thick card or polystyrene

Remember to make the angle of the gnomon equivalent to your latitude, 51.5° for London. [Cutting the gnomon to the lengths shown above will give a gnomon roughly suitable to this country.]

Either mark in the hours by observing the shadow throughout the day or use the table on the next page.

Portable Egyptian shadow clock

These were made of wood.

First thing in the morning, set it facing the Sun so that the shadow of the pencil falls on the crossbar. In the afternoon set it facing west.

The Egyptians included five hour lines plus the noon line.

Plasticine

5 cm

Equal angle sundial

This sundial has hour marks an equal distance apart because its card is aligned with the celestial North Pole.

Take a piece of card and use a protractor to mark lines 15° apart as shown.

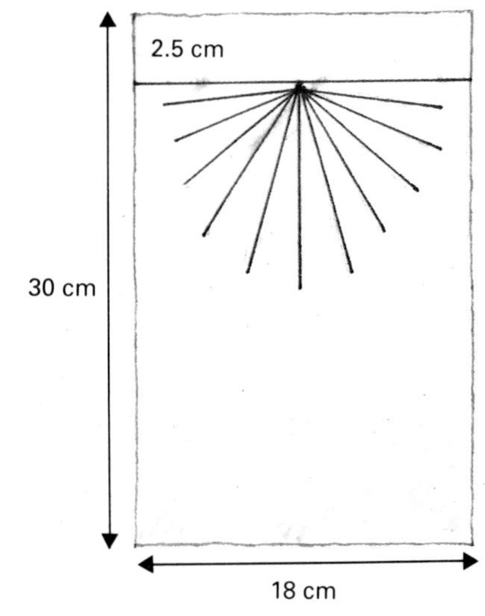

Fix this to a stand with the angle shown at Y equivalent to 90° minus the angle of your latitude. Insert a needle to act as a gnomon.

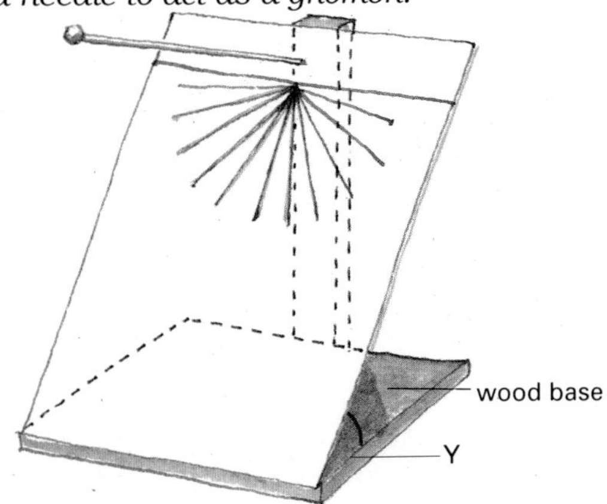

Set the sundial in an east-west direction for use.

Plastic water bottle sundial

This also has equally spaced hour marks.

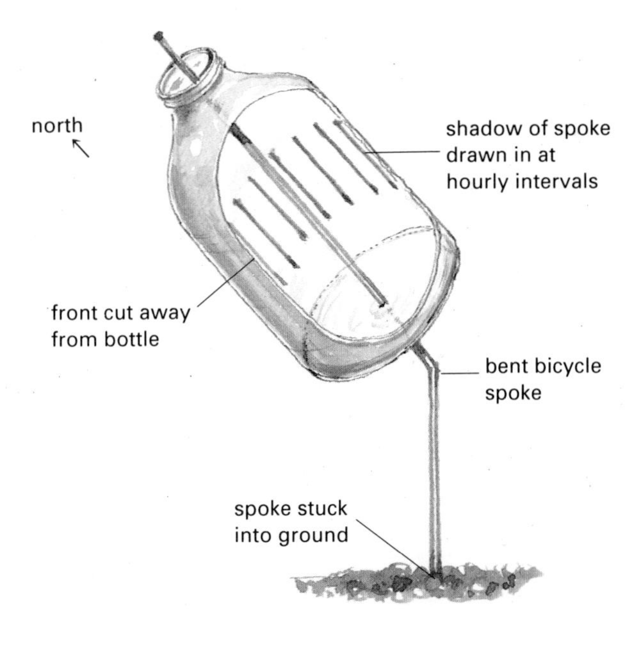

A pocket sundial

Portable pocket sundials were adult toys for the rich. They were made in wood, ivory, brass, and precious metals.

Here is a simple one to make from card. It will fold up and go into an envelope.

Trace the pattern on to stiff card. Cut it out.

Cut along line AB. Score, then bend along lines BC and BD.

C
A
51.5°
cut here
B
bend here
bend here
D
N
W
E
S

Stand triangle ABC up so that it forms a gnomon. Set the sundial with the gnomon aligned with the north-south line, and pointing north.

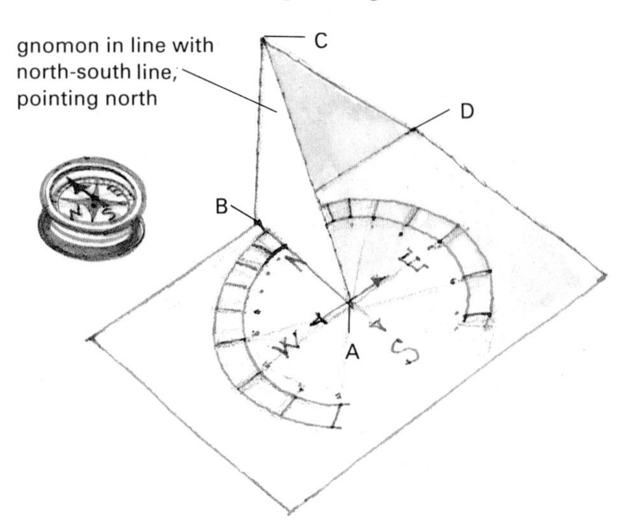

Table for the gradations on the sundial	
Sundial time	Angle for London (latitude 51.5°N)
6 am	0°
7 am	19°
8 am	36.5°
9 am	52°
10 am	65.5°
11 am	78°
12 noon	90°
1 pm	102°
2 pm	114.5°
3 pm	128°
4 pm	143.5°
5 pm	161°
6 pm	180°

Draw the 4 am and 5 am marks diametrically opposite the 4 pm and 5 pm marks, with the 7 pm and 8 pm marks diametrically opposite the 7 am and 8 am ones.

The Sun itself

A plane table and a clinometer make it possible to plot the position of the Sun through the day.

It must be stressed that children should never look directly at the Sun. The Sun's image is cast on to a swivel piece.

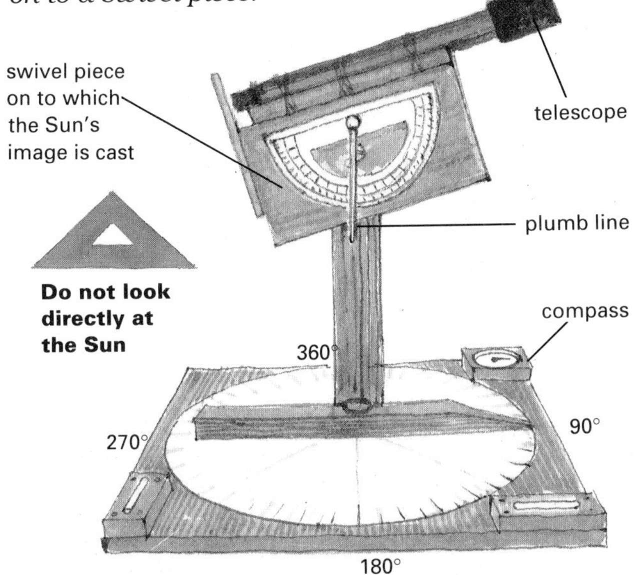

Here is a sample set of results as plotted by children viewing the Sun from their school against prominent features of the immediate landscape.

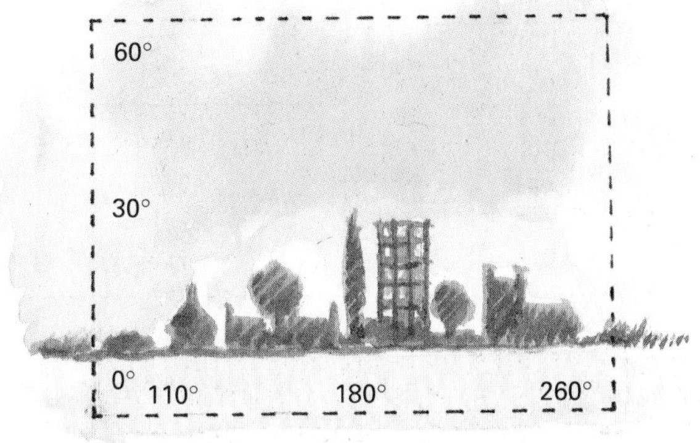

View from the school

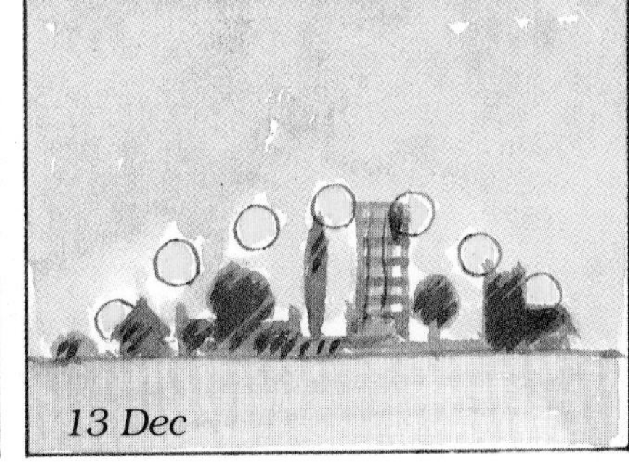

Sun's transit month by month

Discuss the seasons of the year and list some of the things that characterize each one.

Spring	Summer	Autumn	Winter
Lambing	Holidays	Leaf colours	Snow
Daffodils	Sunny days	Bonfires	Robins
Tree foliage			

Make a frieze or a concertina folder to illustrate each season.

What causes the seasons?

The Earth's axis is tilted at an angle of 23.5° to the plane of its orbit around the Sun.

If the Earth were not tilted we would have exactly 12 hours of daylight and 12 hours of darkness, and no seasons.

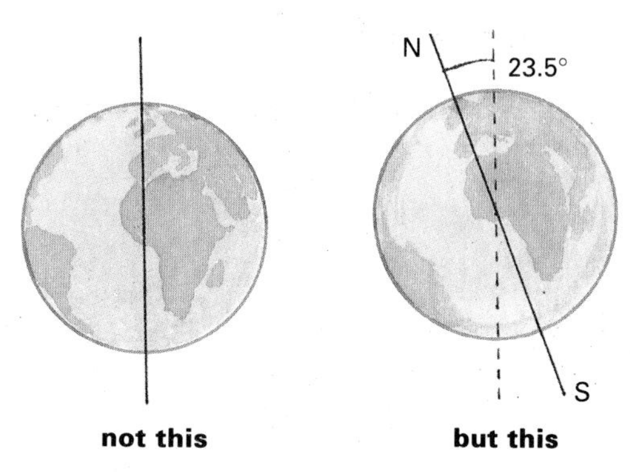

Because the Earth is tilted the number of hours of darkness and of light per day varies through the year and we have seasons.

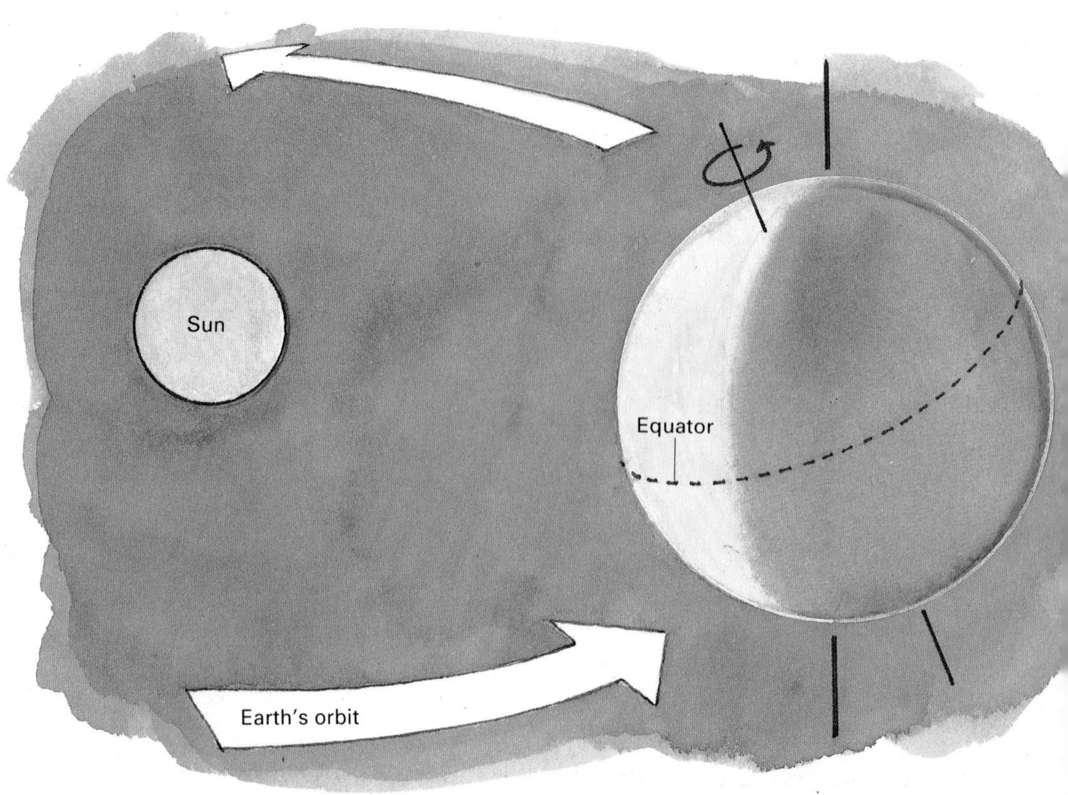

A model of the seasons

Many primary school children find the causes of the seasons difficult to understand. The following is a pictorial explanation, with a suggested simulation using a globe and a torch.

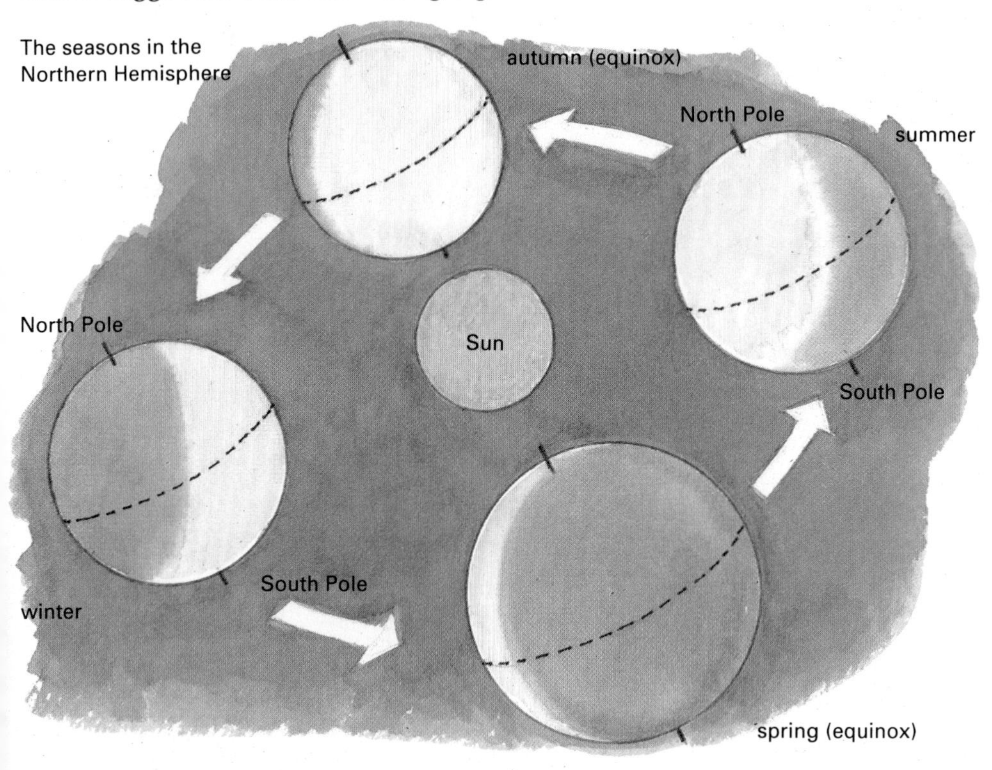

In December when the North Pole is tilted away from the Sun we have winter. In June when the North Pole is tilted towards the Sun we have summer. Halfway between these times the Earth's axis lies at right angles to the Sun and we have equal day and night – the equinoxes.

It is as well to remember that not all parts of the Earth have seasons like us. At the Poles there are extremes of day and night between summer and winter, and at the Equator there are only wet and dry seasons.

The height of the Sun in the sky as observed from Earth varies with the seasons. This affects both the number of hours of daylight and the temperature (see pages 55 and 59).

Take a globe of the world on a stand. It is fixed at an angle of 23.5°. Set it to each of the four positions shown below, in a darkened room. Shine a torch at the globe for each of the four positions while someone turns it slowly and note the areas in the Northern Hemisphere that are in light and in darkness. One will have more light than darkness, one will have more darkness than light, and two positions will have equal light and dark.

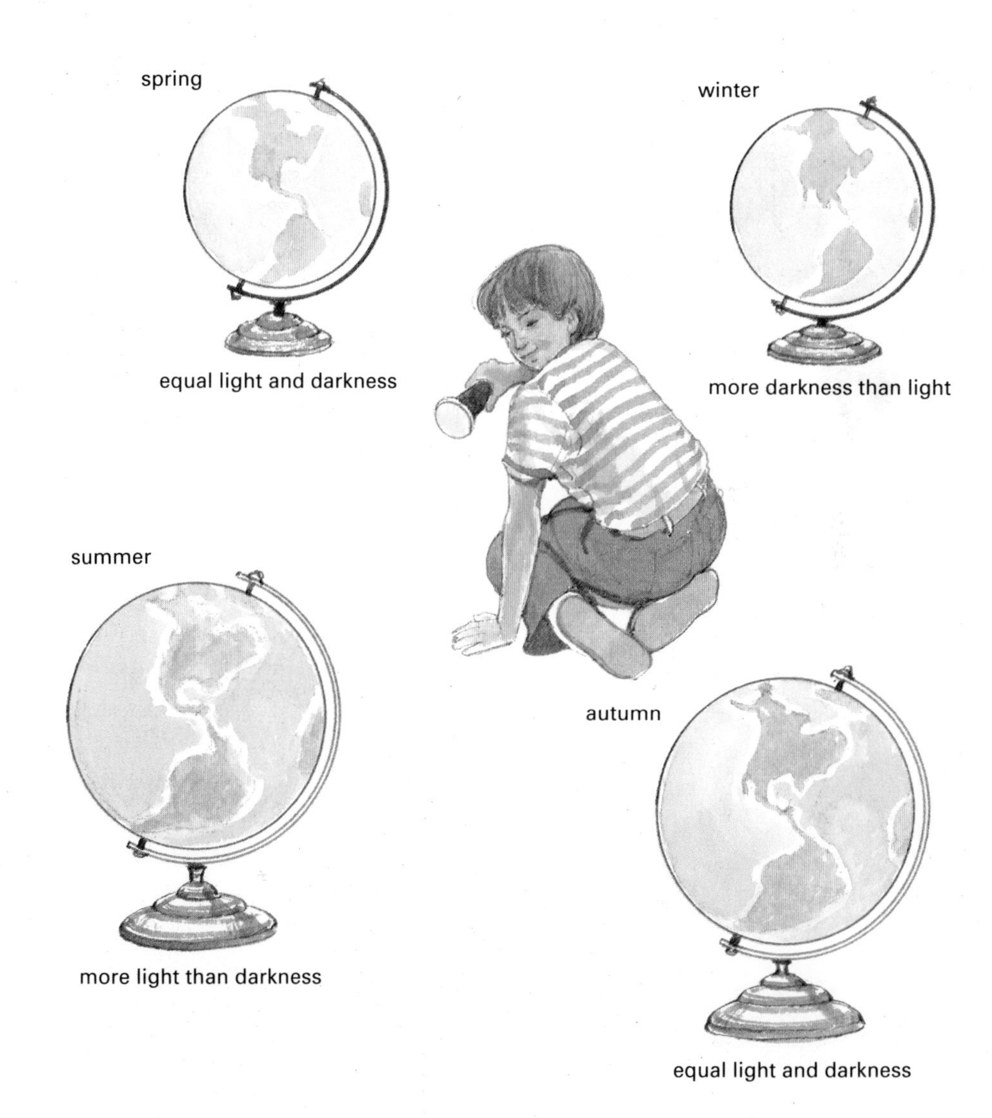

The Sun is our source of light and heat. It is the centre of our solar system around which all the planets revolve. It is, of course, a star and it is the nearest star to us. It is 1392,000 km in diameter and occupies a space equivalent to about one million Earths. It generates energy by nuclear fusion of atoms within itself. The temperature on the surface is 6000°C; inside, it may reach 15,000°C.

Observing the Sun

It is dangerous to look directly at the Sun, but you can project a safe image of it on to a piece of white card through a telescope or a pair of binoculars.

Do not look directly at the Sun

Use a clamp, or some sort of support, to hold the card steady.

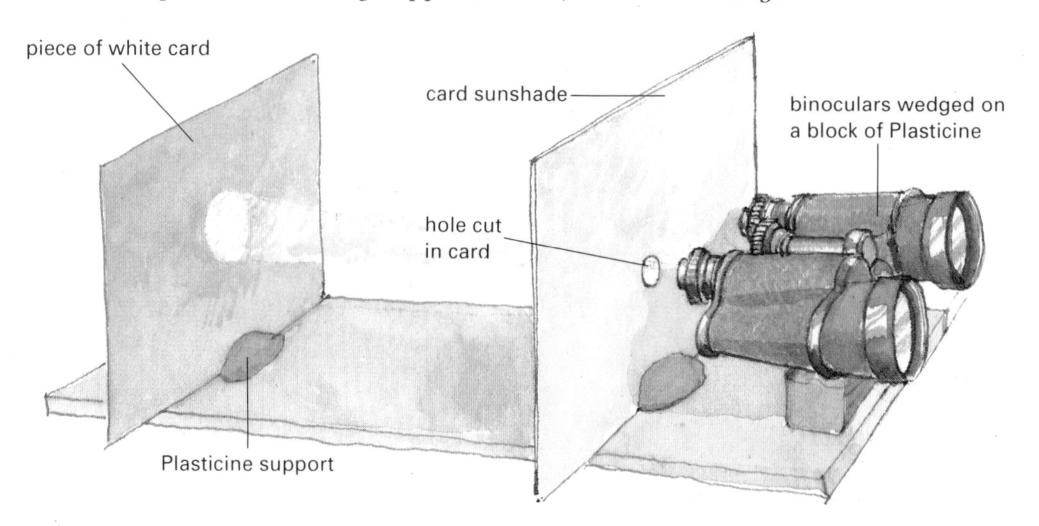

Sunspots, which are dark patches on the Sun's surface that may cover an area of several thousand square kilometres, will show up on the image. These spots on the sun are up to 2000°C cooler than surrounding areas. They appear singly, in pairs or in groups, with a maximum activity period every eleven years. Daily observation will show change in size and show that the Sun rotates on its axis. Weekly observation will give an idea of their activity over time.

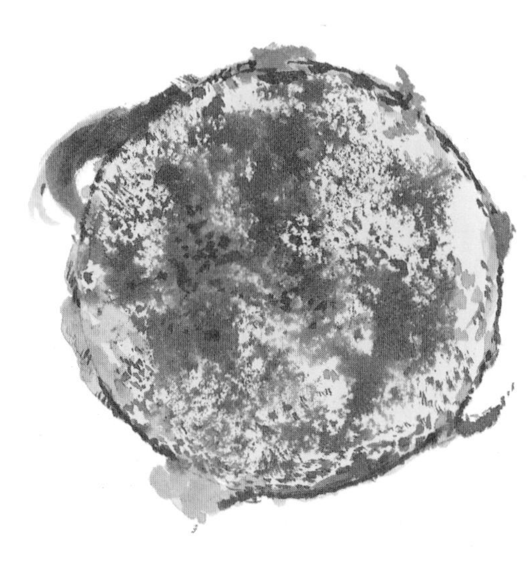

Sunrise and sunset

The times of sunrise and sunset vary with the seasons. 'Whitaker's Almanack' gives times for the first of each month. They are also given in some diaries.

Plotting the times of sunrise and sunset for the first day of each month through the year gives a graph like the one below.

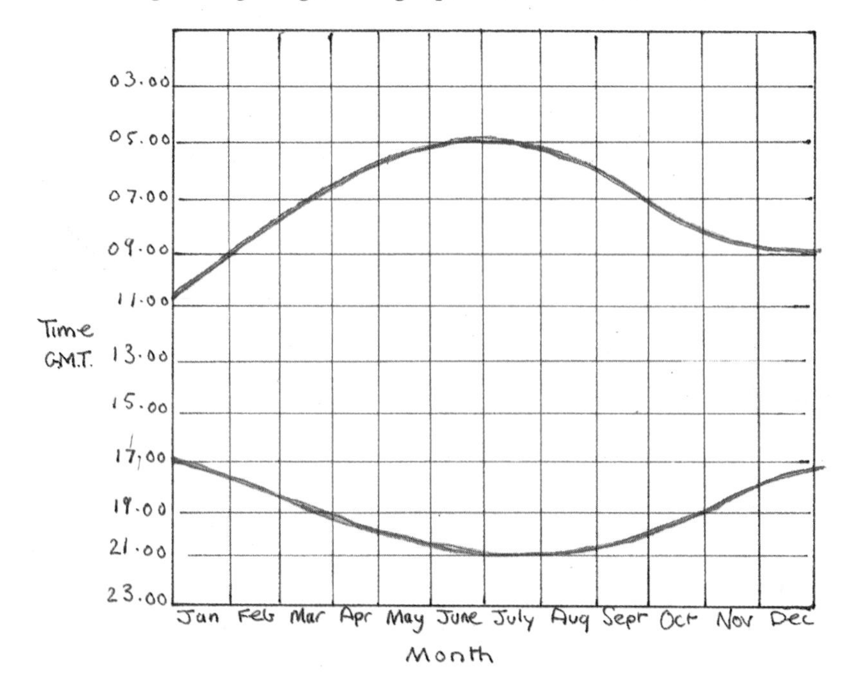

The height of the Sun in the sky as observed from Earth varies with the seasons.

We are used to the short days of midwinter when the Sun is low in the sky and only appears above the horizon for a few hours. The Sun's rays do not heat the Earth as much as they do in summer because the warmth is spread over a wider area, so the days are cold.

In midsummer the Sun is at its highest point in the northern sky and it stays above the horizon longer than in the winter. There are more hours of daylight. The Sun's rays are concentrated on a smaller area, and the days are consequently warmer.

In March and September at the equinoxes, the Sun's height in the sky is midway between that of winter and summer and we have approximately equal lengths of daylight and darkness. The angle at which the Sun's rays hit the Earth is between that shown for winter and summer, and the temperature is also between the two extremes.

Sun's position through the year

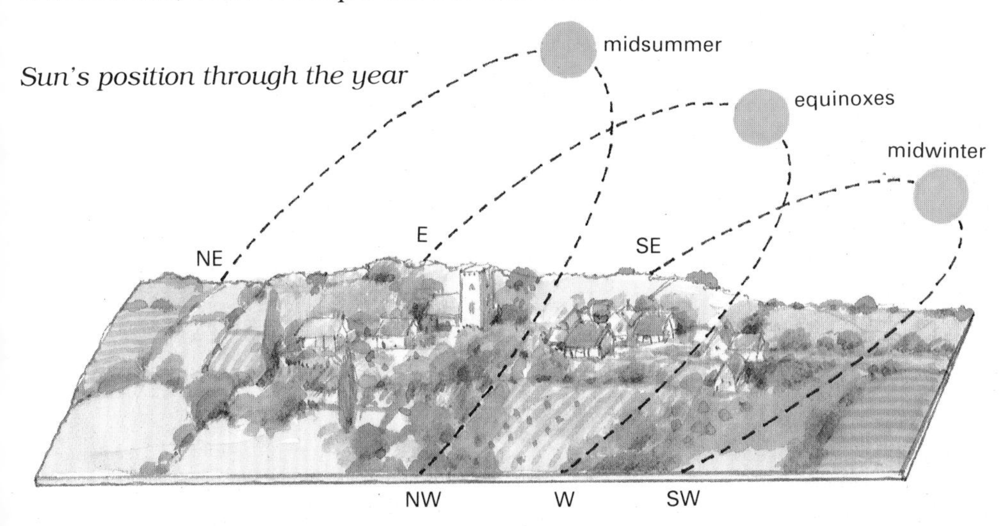

Sun's heating effect through the year

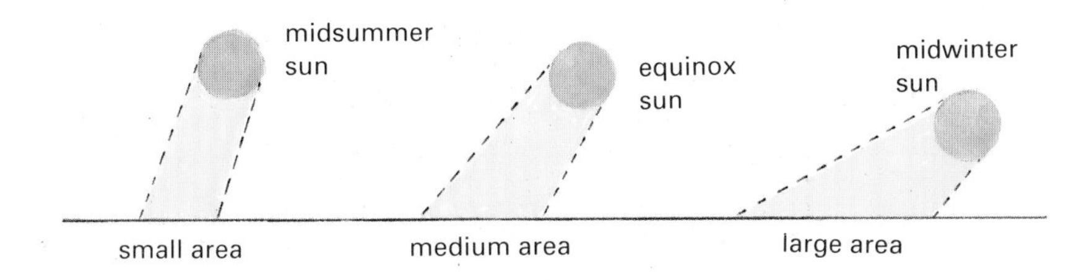

Children can demonstrate for themselves the effect that is obtained angling rays of light.

The heating effect of the Sun's rays falling fairly directly and falling at an angle can be shown.

Shine the light and heat from a light bulb on to a thermometer <u>*under*</u> *a square of black felt, which represents the Earth's surface. Use two similar lamps but beam the light directly from one, and at an angle from the other.*

Which thermometer heats up the most?

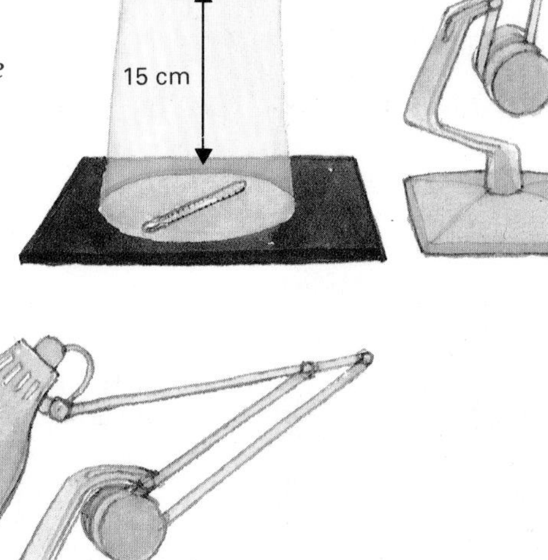

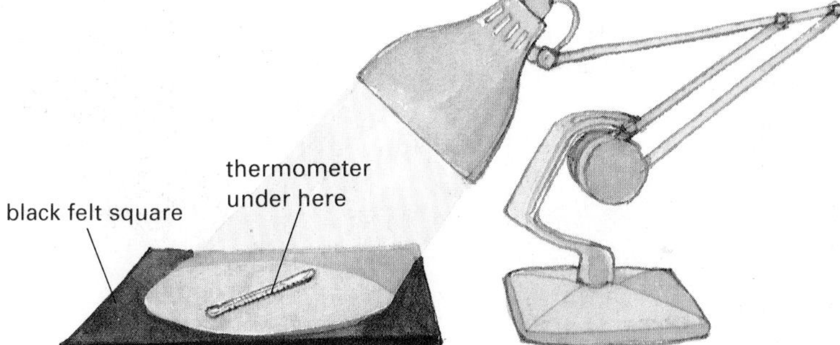

Solar heating

The use of solar panels to capture energy from the Sun is becoming more widespread.

Investigate the heating ability of the Sun. You will need four small identical jam jars.

1 *Cover one jar with aluminium kitchen foil, one jar with black paper, and one jar half with aluminium foil and half with black paper.*

Leave the fourth jar clear as a control.

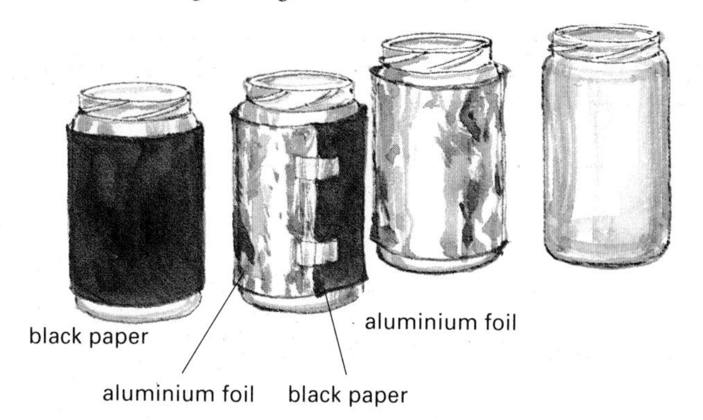

2 *Put 50 ml of water into each jar.*

3 *Take the temperature of the water in each jar. Keep a record.*

4 *Put the beakers on a sunny windowsill. The jar covered with half aluminium foil and half black paper should have the black paper facing the sun and the foil facing the room.*

Black paper absorbs heat, aluminium foil reflects heat (see 'An Early Start to Energy', page 36 and 43).

5 *Record the temperatures of the water in the jars every 10 minutes.*

	Temperature			
Time (mins)	Foil	Black paper	B.Paper + Foil	Control
10				
20				
30				
40				

Plot a graph showing temperature against time.

Many modern homes have large south-facing windows and small north-facing ones. Often there is a conservatory on the south side, and sometimes black solar panels on the roof. All these help to capture heat from the Sun.

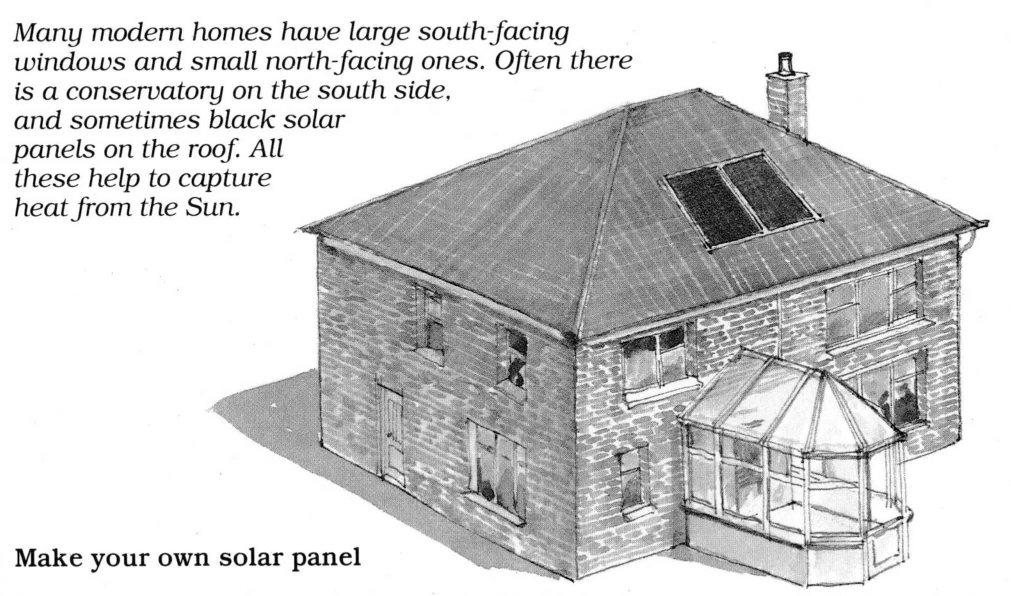

Make your own solar panel

Remember that dull and dark colours absorb heat, but shiny, light coloured surfaces reflect heat.

You will need the materials shown.

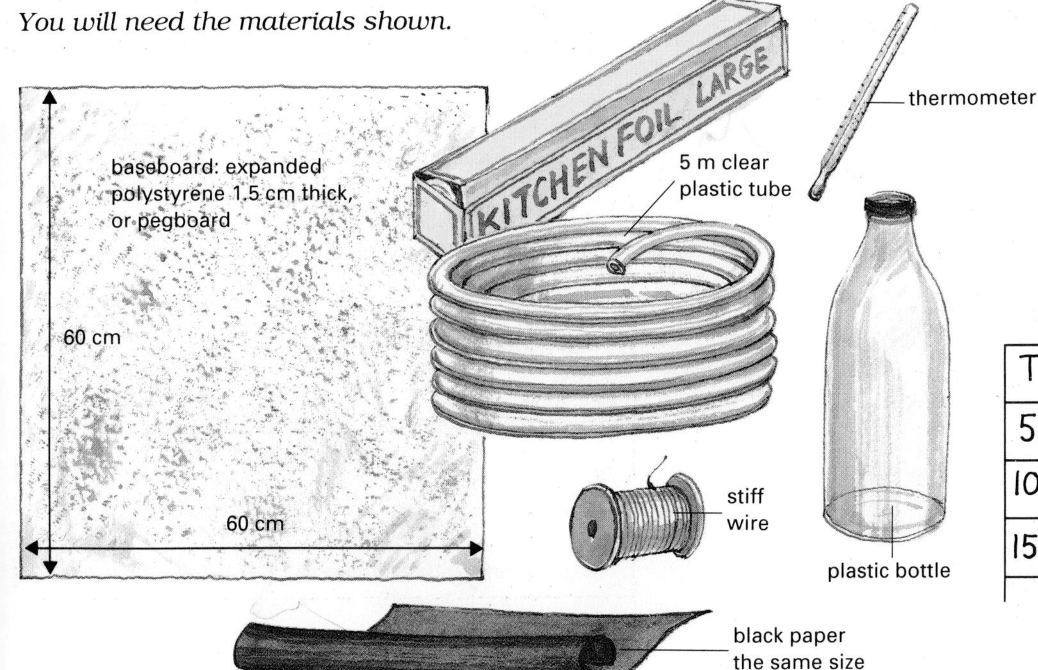

1 *Cover the baseboard with kitchen foil.*

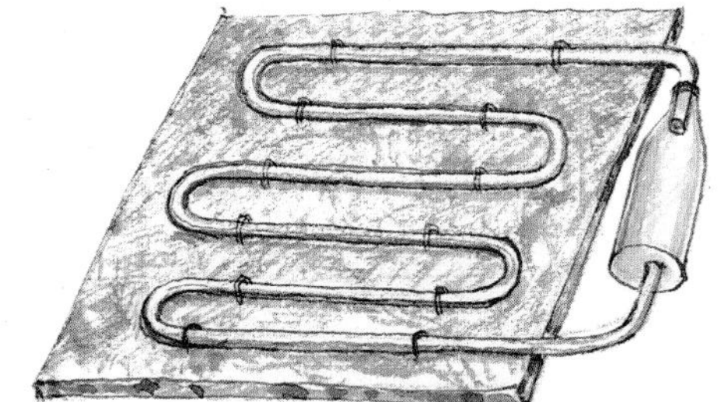

2 *Pin the clear plastic tubing to the baseboard in a zigzag shape with the wire.*

3 *Make a very small hole in the bottom of the bottle so that it will not leak when you insert the lower end of the tubing. The upper end should project a short way into the top of the bottle.*

4 *Fill the system completely with water. Cover the heater panel with a sheet of black paper. Place it in the sunlight.*

black paper

water up to top of bottle

5 *Record the temperature at 5 minute intervals for 1 hour.*

Time	At top of bottle	At bottom of bottle
5 mins		
10 mins		
15 mins		

Time	Air temp. in shade
5 mins	
10 mins	
15 mins	

See 'An Early Start to Technology', page 73, for details of how to make a solar cooker.

'And God called the light day', and the darkness he called night. And the evening and the morning were the first day. [Genesis 1:5]

Timekeeping is based on a natural phenomenon – the rotation of the Earth, giving an interval of one day.

The Earth spins like a top. The part facing the Sun is in daylight. The part facing away from the Sun is in night.

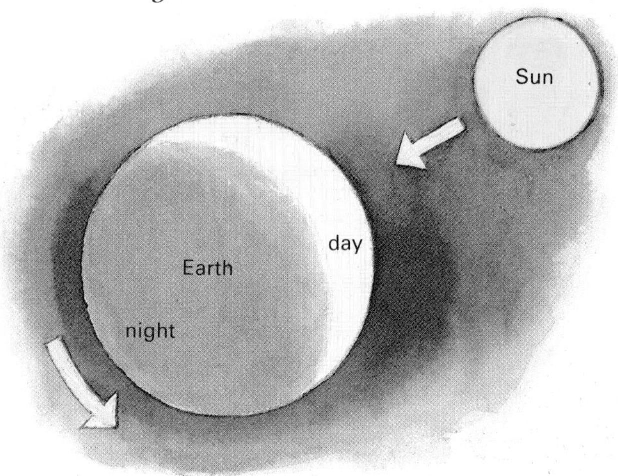

This can be demonstrated in a darkened room.

Turn the ball slowly.

Timekeeping around the world

A discussion with the children on how other societies measure the passage of time is a good lead into thinking about timekeeping.

The Comanches of North America drew hieroglyphs. A three-day journey would be shown by three circles representing Suns.

Make up some hieroglyphs of your own. Cut a tally stick.

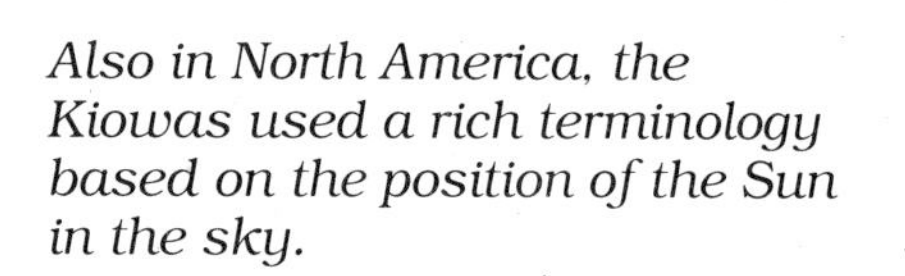

Also in North America, the Kiowas used a rich terminology based on the position of the Sun in the sky.

- *Dawn – literally 'first light'*
- *Sunrise – literally 'the sun has come up'*
- *Morning – literally 'full day'*
- *Noon*
- *Early afternoon (until 3 o'clock)*
- *Late afternoon*
- *Evening – literally 'first darkness'*

The Inuit of Greenland reckoned time by the ebb and flow of the tides.

The Pawnees used to cut notches in a stick to mark the passage of the nights. They denoted night by the word 'sleep'.

The Romans were the first to use night watches of a fixed length in their army.

The English names for the days of the week are derived from the Saxon, the French from the Latin.

Days of the week

Saxon	English
Sun's day	Sunday
Moon's day	Monday
Tiw's day (Norse god of war)	Tuesday
Woden's day (Norse god of storms)	Wednesday
Thor's day (Norse god of thunder)	Thursday
Frigg's day (Wife of Odin)	Friday
Sæter's day (Saturn – Roman god of Agriculture)	Saturday

Latin	French
Dies Solis (Sun's day)	Dimanche
Dies Lunæ (Moon's day)	Lundi
Dies Martis (Mar's day god of war)	Mardi
Dies Mercurii (Mercury's day – messenger of the gods)	Mercredi
Dies Jovis (Jove or Jupiter's day – ruler of the gods)	Jeudi
Dies Veneris (Venus' day)	Vendredi
Dies Saturni (Saturn's day – god of agriculture)	Samedi

One complete spin of the Earth takes about 24 hours. This takes the Earth through 360°, so in 1 hour it turns through 15° ($=\frac{360}{24}$).

Ask children to draw a circle and mark it at 15° intervals.

They will find they have 24 segments. Each marks a time zone.

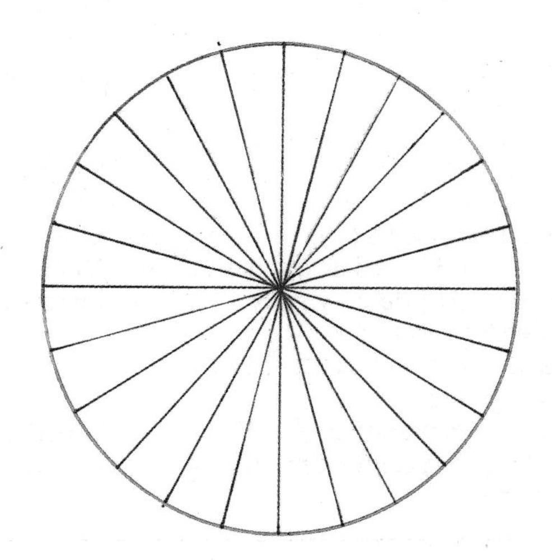

As the Earth spins, zones pass from darkness into light. The spinning causes the day to pass. Every 15° takes 1 hour.

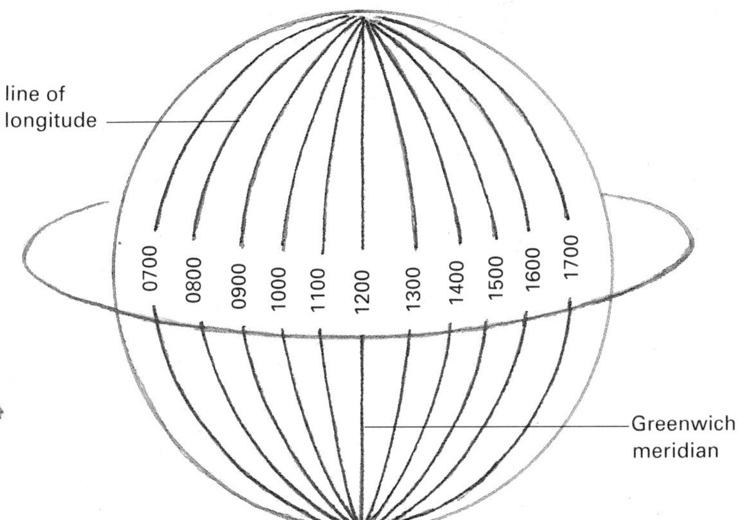

Greenwich Observatory

Much of the pioneer work in astronomy and in timekeeping stems from the Royal Observatory at Greenwich. By international agreement in 1884 the line of longitude passing through Greenwich was declared the prime meridian and all time measured from it.

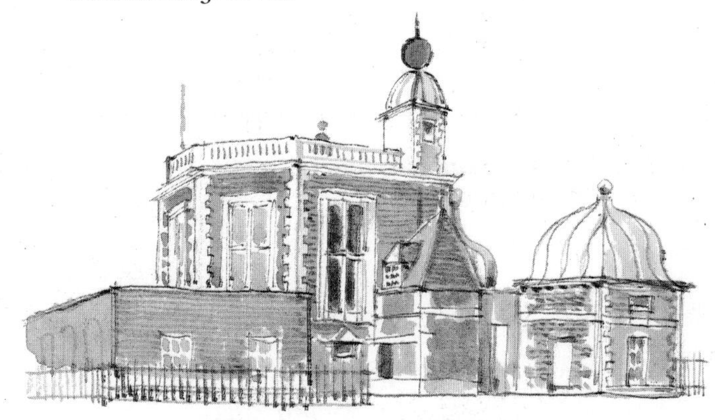

Because the Earth spins from west to east, places west of Greenwich have their time later than in Greenwich.

Here is an example. New York is about 75° west of Greenwich. So it is about 5 hours ($=\frac{75}{15}$) behind Greenwich.

Use a globe of the world to look up the longitude of large towns and cities. Work out the time in each place when it is noon in Greenwich.

Place	Longitude	Time
San Francisco	120° W	04 00
Canberra	150° E	22 00
Rome	15° E	01 00
Accra	0°	12 00

The Moon takes about $27\frac{1}{3}$ days to go around the Earth. That is the time from the point of view of an astronaut in space. But because the Earth is also moving around the Sun it takes $29\frac{1}{2}$ days before we on Earth see the Moon in the same position relative to the Sun. This is called a lunation or lunar month; the true time is called a synodical month.

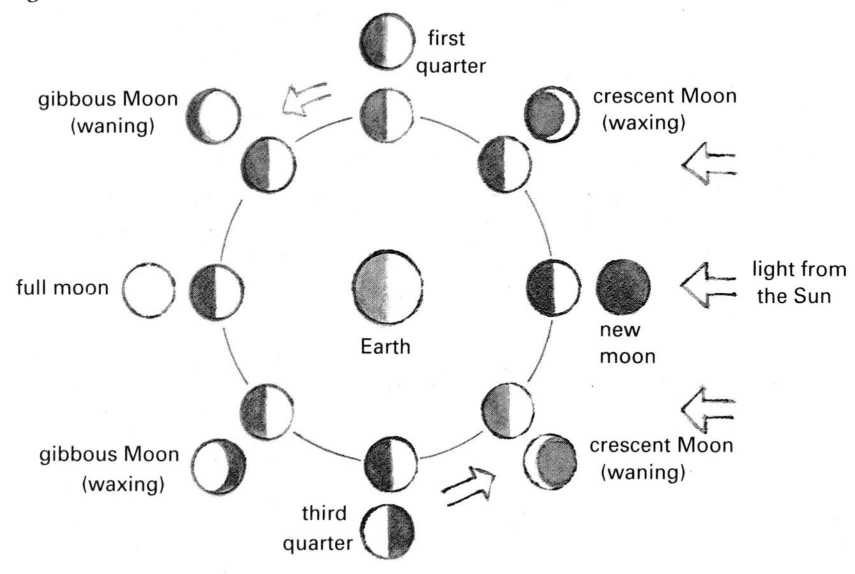

The outer ring of sketches shows the Moon as it appears in the sky.

See 'An Early Start to Nature', page 60, for ways of plotting the Moon through the month.

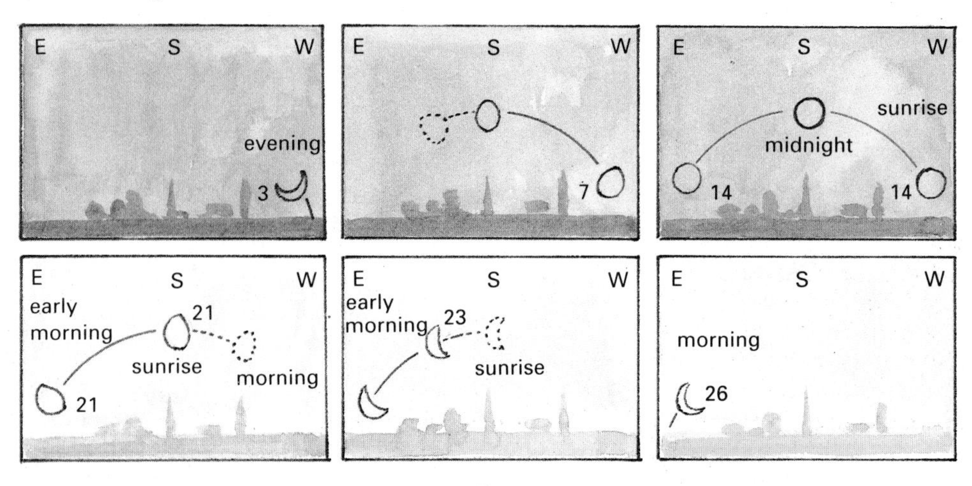

Twelve lunations take 354 days. This differs by about $11\frac{1}{4}$ days from the solar year. (The solar year is the time the Earth takes to go around the Sun, just under $365\frac{1}{4}$ days.) Our western calendar divides the year into conventional months. These are quite independent of the Moon and keep, as a reminder of their origin, only a name and a length approximating to that of the Moon's revolution.

Months of the year

January – after the double faced Roman god Janus, who looks into both past and future
February – after Februa, a Roman festival of purification
March – after Mars, the Roman god of war
April – connected with Latin aperire, 'to open', because it is a spring month
May – after Maia, the Roman goddess of growth
June – after the Roman tribe of Junius, and connected with Juno, queen of the gods
July – after Julius Caesar, who named it after himself
August – after Augustus Caesar, who wanted his own month too – and stole a day from February so that his month was 31 days as well
September – after Latin septem, 'seven', because the old Roman year began in March
October – after Latin octo, 'eight'
November – after Latin novem, 'nine'
December – after Latin decem, 'ten'

The Egyptians

The ancient Egyptians had a calendar of 12 months, each of 30 days, with 5 supplementary days added at the end of each year. Using this method a quarter of a day is lost every year. This year is called 'vague' because with the passage of time the lost quarter days accumulate and the year starts earlier and earlier. The Muslim calendar still wanders in this way.

The Israelites

The ancient Jewish calendar is based on the Moon. The year has 12 months, each of 29 or 30 days, with the insertion of a 13th month 7 times during each 19 year period.

The natural year is the time taken for the Earth to pass around the Sun:
365 days, 5 hours, 48 minutes, 46 seconds.

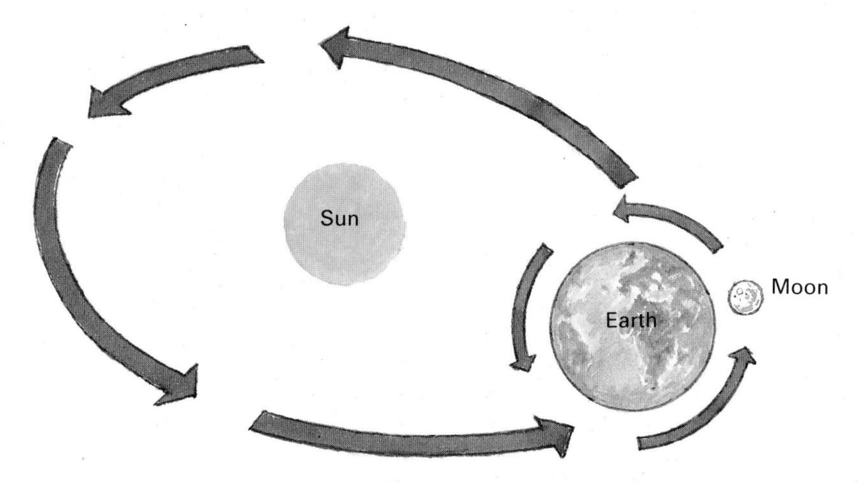

It is an awkward unit of time, and a calendar has evolved where the days of the year are divided between the months and any odd time left over is mopped up in leap years. Many of us resort to the old rhyme to help us remember how many days in each month.

Thirty days hath September,
April, June and November,
All the rest have thirty-one
Excepting February alone
Which hath but twenty-eight days clear,
And twenty-nine in each leap year.

Make a survey of special dates. Collect information from the children. Look up diaries.

Birthdays	Holidays	National anniversaries	Festivals
	Xmas Day	Guy Fawkes	
		Thanksgiving	

Put everything in date order.

A world calendar

In order to make dates easier to deal with it has been suggested that we have a world calendar. Birthdays and other events would always fall on the same day of the week and we would not need to reprint the calendar.
January, April, July and October have 31 days. All other months have 30 days. This makes a total of 364 days.

The 365th day, called Worldsday, comes at the end of December; it would be a universal holiday.

In leap years an extra day is added at the end of June.

There are four quarters to the year, beginning on the first of January. Each quarter starts on a Sunday and ends on a Saturday.

What do children think of such a calendar?

January, April, July, October

S	M	T	W	T	F	S
1	2	3	4	5	6	7
8	9	10	11	12	13	14
15	16	17	18	19	20	21
22	23	24	25	26	27	28
29	30	31				

February, May, August, November

S	M	T	W	T	F	S
			1	2	3	4
5	6	7	8	9	10	11
12	13	14	15	16	17	18
19	20	21	22	23	24	25
26	27	28	29	30		

March, September, December

S	M	T	W	T	F	S
					1	2
3	4	5	6	7	8	9
10	11	12	13	14	15	16
17	18	19	20	21	22	23
24	25	26	27	28	29	30

June

S	M	T	W	T	F	S
					1	2
3	4	5	6	7	8	9
10	11	12	13	14	15	16
17	18	19	20	21	22	23
24	25	26	27	28	29	30
						[L]

Special astronomical dates

Children could look up the dates when the length of day and night are equal, the equinox. They could also find out the date for the longest day (Summer solstice), Midsummer's Day, and the shortest day (Winter solstice).

The spring (or vernal) equinox – March 21 or 22
The longest day, Summer solstice – June 21 or 22
The autumnal equinox – September 21 or 22
The shortest day, Winter solstice – December 21 or 22

Children can look at the Moon through binoculars. It is an exciting thing to do because it reveals fine detail. Resting arms on a wall helps keep the binoculars as still as possible.

The main features are the rolling plains, the maria, which usually appear darker than surrounding areas; the craters; and the mountain ranges.

There are a number of source books that have photographs of the Moon, including the side away from the Earth. These make good material to supplement actual Moon watching.

The craters are named after famous astronomers and scientists, like Plato, Archimedes and Copernicus. Mountain ranges are named after ranges on Earth, for example Alps, Appenines and Carpathian Mountains. Maria have fanciful names like Mare Humboldtianum, Mare Humorum and Mare Serenitatis.

Tides

The Moon orbits the Earth at an average distance of 384,400 km. The nearer a mass is to the Moon the more strongly it is pulled by the mass of the Moon. Thus it is that we have the rise and fall of the tides twice a day.

The ocean shown at A in the diagram is nearer to the Moon than the solid sphere of the Earth and it is therefore pulled more strongly towards the Moon. This results in a large bulge forming in the ocean. At point B in the diagram the ocean is farther from the Moon than the solid part of the Earth. Again this results in a bulge in the ocean. The bulges stay in line with the Moon.

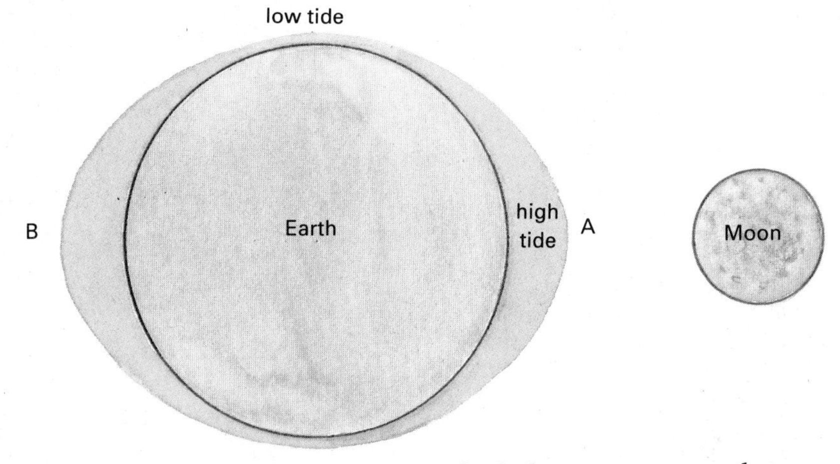

However, because the Earth is spinning the bulges move around the Earth in the opposite direction. When a bulge reaches a place, that place has a high tide. Since there are two bulges, there are two high tides and two low tides each day.

Why tides vary

The Sun also exerts a gravitational pull on the Earth. If the Sun and Moon are in line, the high tides are higher; these are called 'spring tides'. If the Sun and Moon are at 90° to each other, the gravitational forces work against each other and we have lower 'neap tides'.

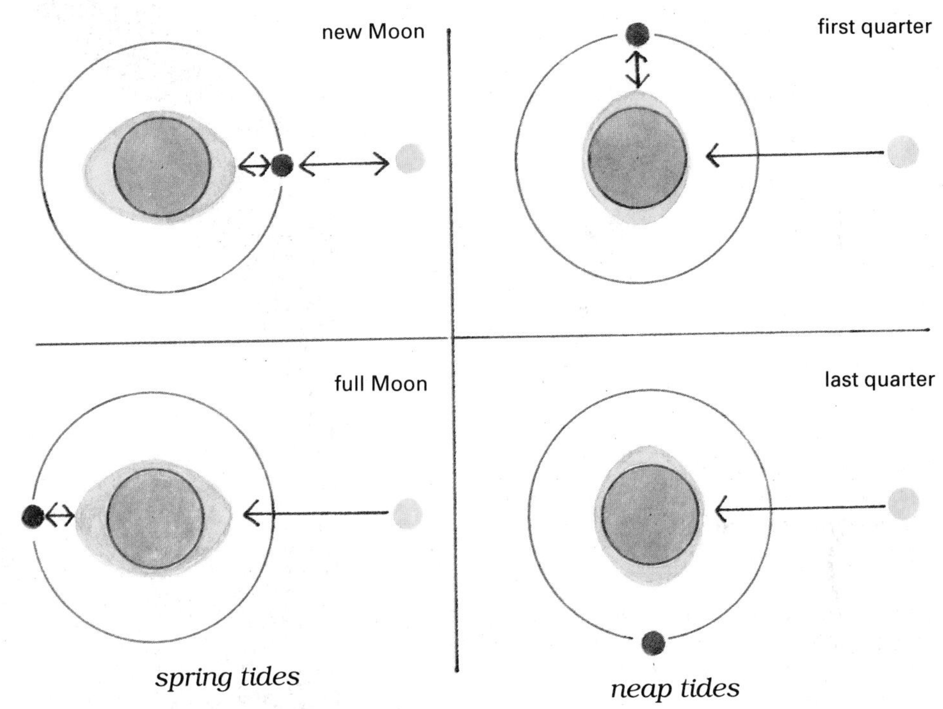

Schools in coastal areas can check the tides against published tide tables, and examine the tables to see how the tides vary through the year.

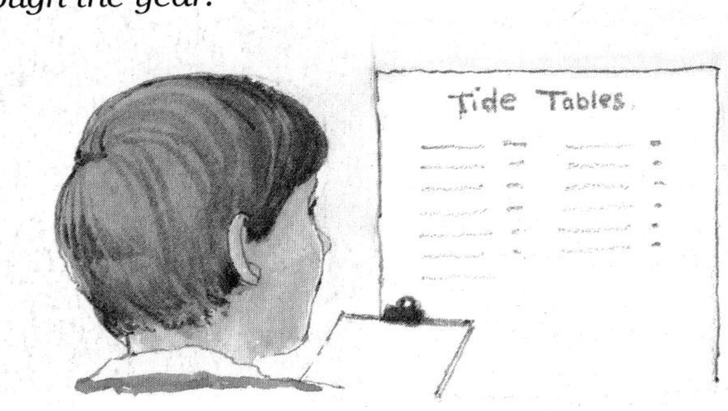

The key concept in any study of time with children is developing the idea of the duration of events, and measuring such events. Inventing clocks to measure events is not only fun but takes children into problem solving and into technology.

The timing problem can be an open one, for example:
'Choose any time between 5 and 50 seconds and make as accurate a timer as you can to measure that time. Use any of these materials, plus water if you need it.'

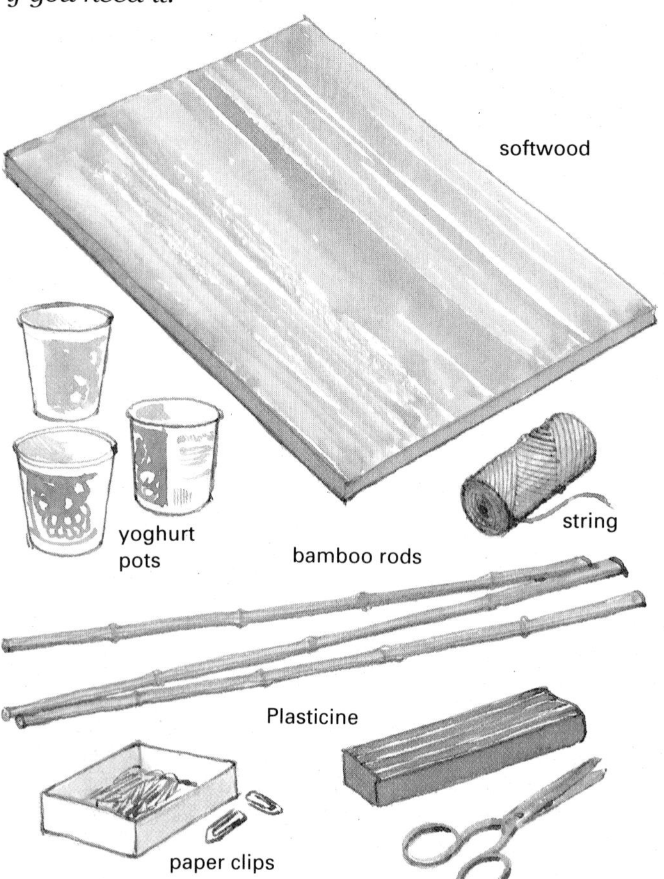

'An Early Start to Science', page 25, features some simple water, sand and candle clocks. Here are more suggestions for timers.

A marble rolling down a slope

How many:
pin-men
words
crosses
can you make before the marble runs its course?

Try making the route so that the marble takes:
10 seconds
15 seconds
20 seconds
to traverse it.

Experiment with the variables
1 *The height of the slope*

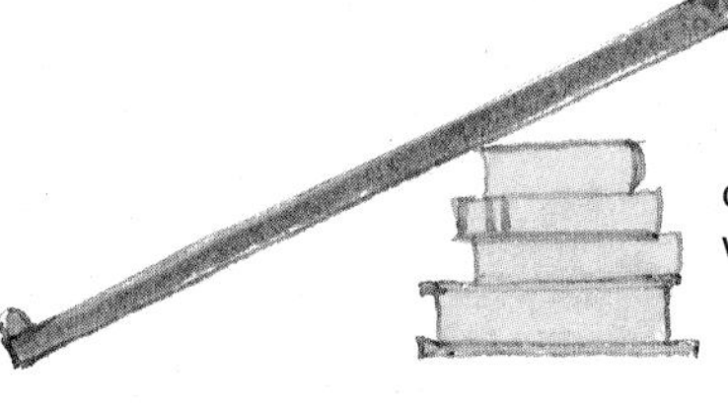

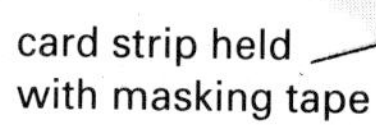

2 *The size of the ball*
Use balls made from Plasticine

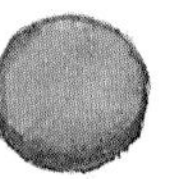

3 *The heaviness of the balls*
Make sure the size is constant.

Try it on a larger scale with a table tilted on books.

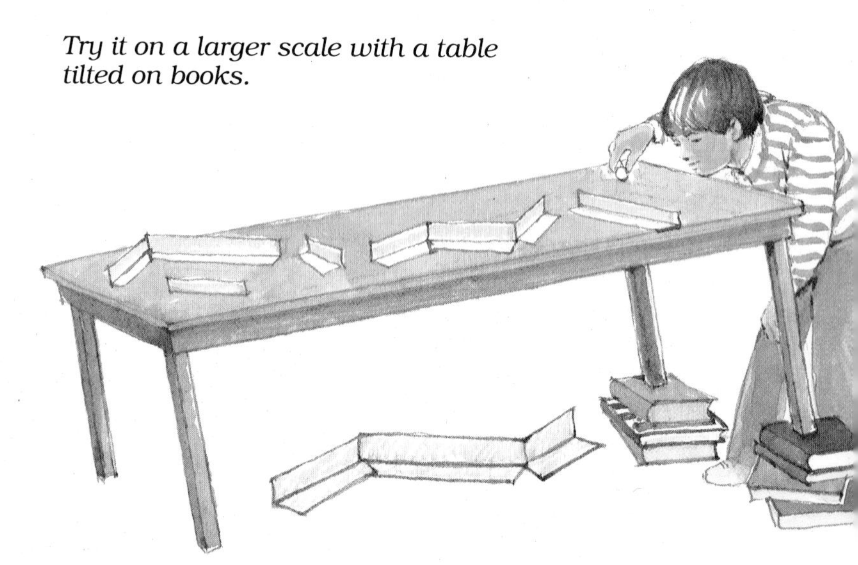

The pendulum

The pendulum is a common timing device.

The main factors to investigate in time of swing of a pendulum are:

- *the size of the bob*
- *the size of the swing (i.e. big swings/little swings)*
- *whether the pendulum is given a push*
- *the length of the string*

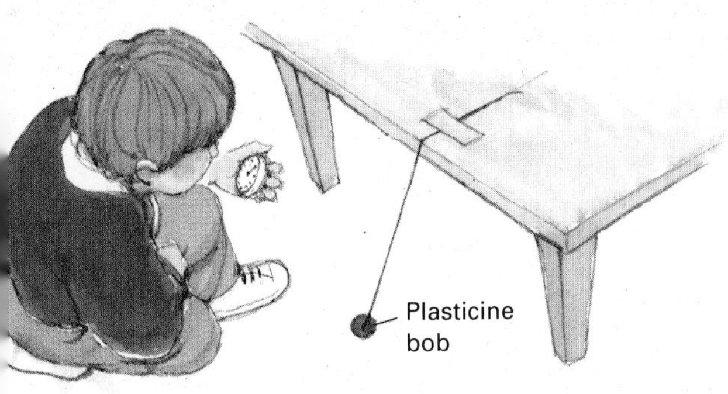

Investigate each in turn by timing 20 swings of the pendulum.
Leave the length of the string until last.

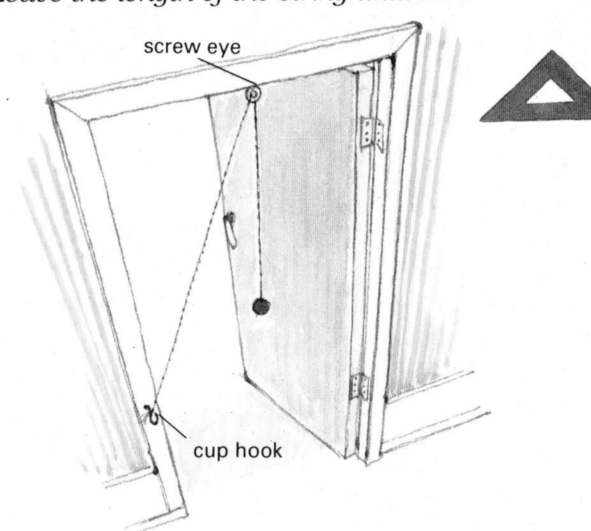

Children will find that the only effective variable is the length of the string.

Plot a graph of time against length by gradually increasing the length of the pendulum to a good 10 to 20 cm over 1 metre.

Read off from the graph the length of a seconds pendulum – that is, a pendulum that swings from right to left in 1 second. (It is approximately 1 metre long.)

Alarm clocks

Here are some candle alarms.

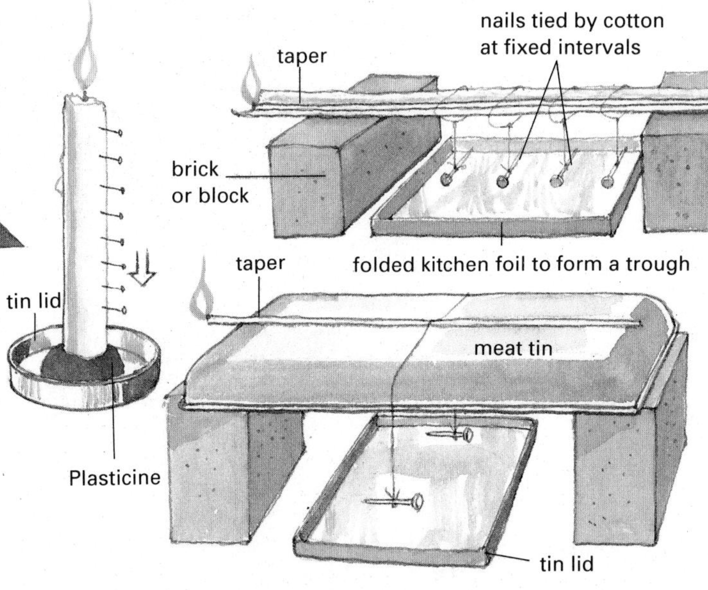

In each case the falling pin or nail will make a noise.

A water alarm

This consists of a cork or polystyrene float covered in aluminium kitchen foil, which rises in a container to make a connection across two bare wires and thus complete an electric circuit. This causes a buzzer to sound or a bulb to light.

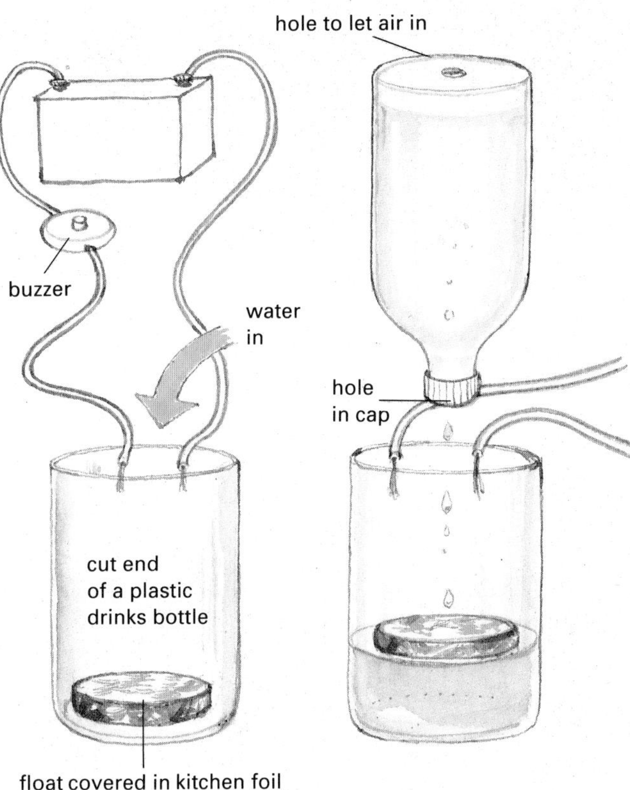

The trick is to control the rate at which water flows into the container so that it completes the circuit in a fixed time. Water can be made to run in from a plastic bottle as long as there is a hole in the other end to let the air in.

A subsidiary technical problem is to suspend the bottle. A clamp will do, but good technology could come from making a stand from wood or Meccano.

The name planet comes from the Greek word for 'wanderer', because of the way the planets move slowly across the background of stars. In our solar system there are nine planets orbiting the Sun. The orbits of the planets are shown in the illustration below. Pluto is usually the most distant planet from the Sun, but its orbit is eccentric and every so often it crosses inside Neptune's orbit for a few Earth years – the last time this happened was at the end of the 1980s. The planets do not give off any light of their own. We can see them because they are lit by the Sun.

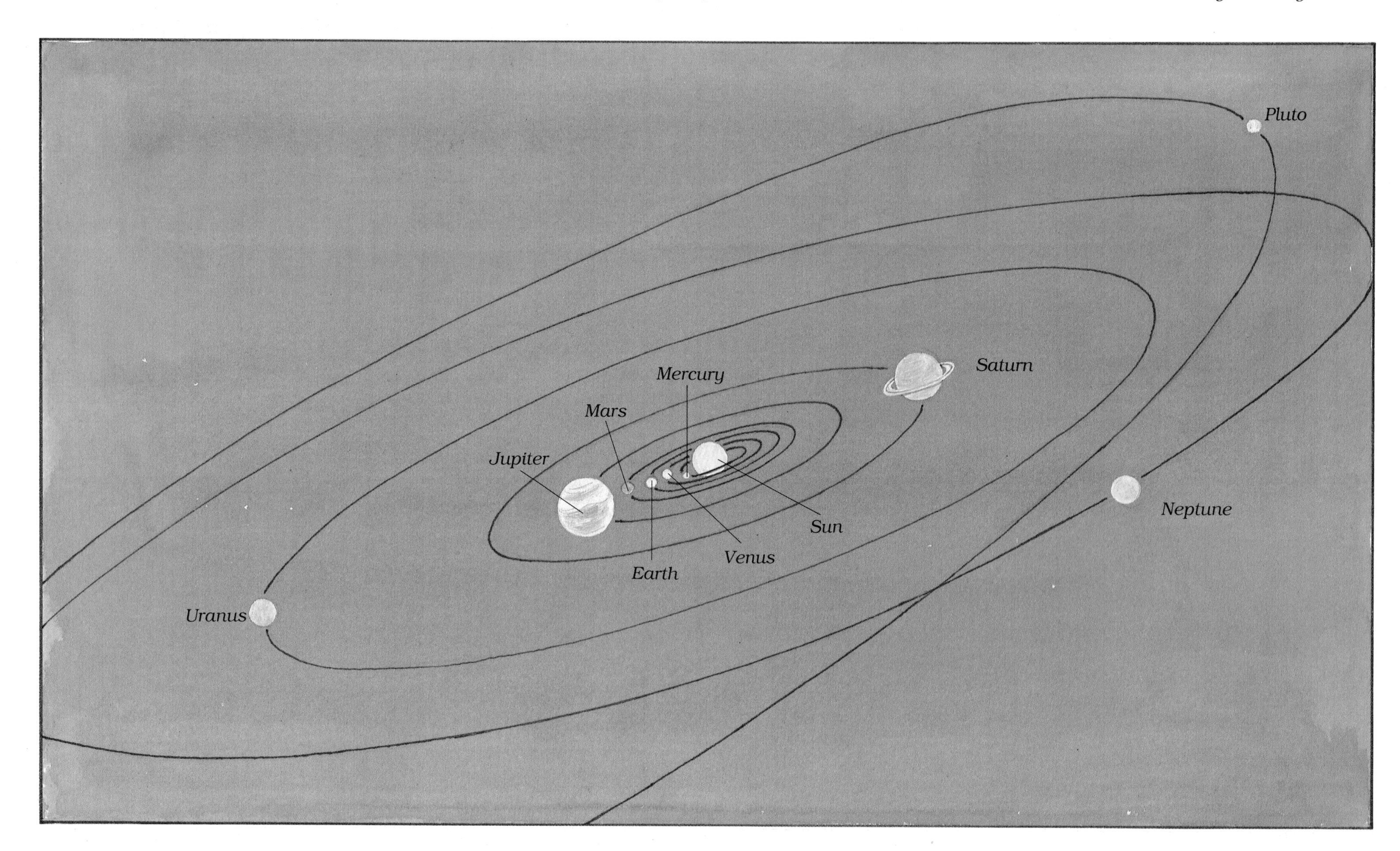

Draw the planets in 2D to scale on paper.

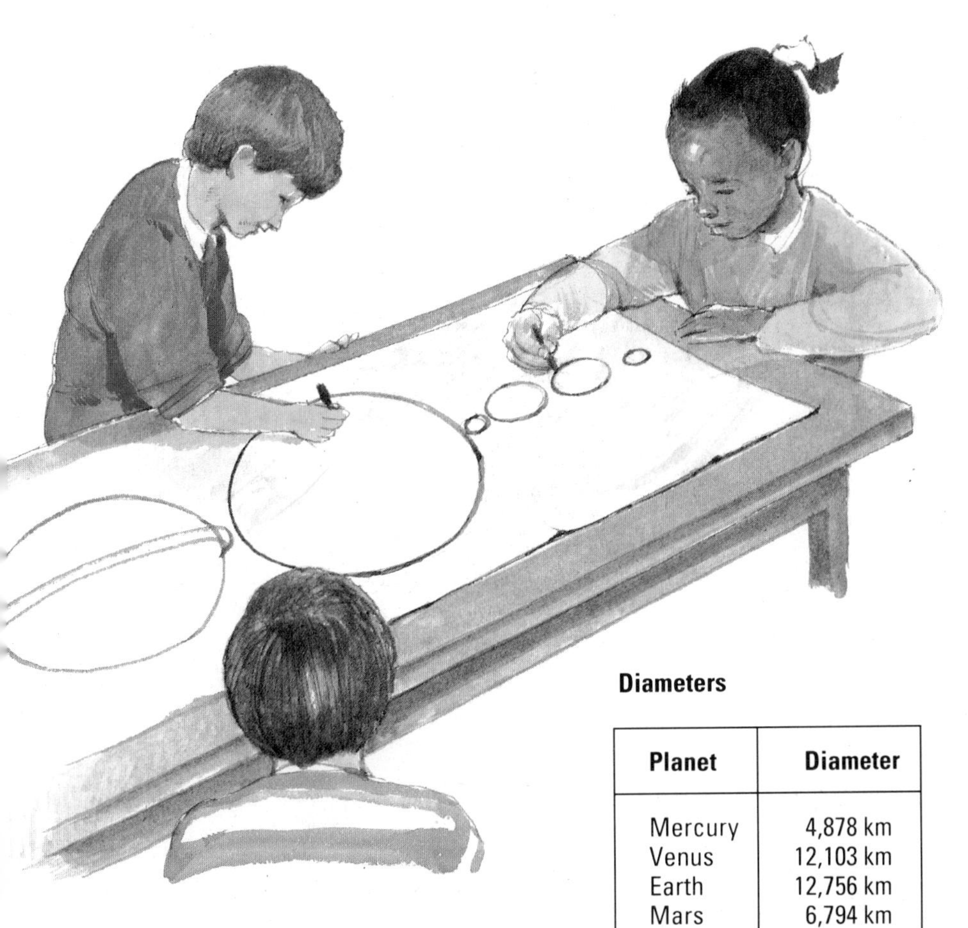

Make the planets in 3D as papier-mâché objects. Hang them from the ceiling when decorated.

Diameters

Planet	Diameter
Mercury	4,878 km
Venus	12,103 km
Earth	12,756 km
Mars	6,794 km
Jupiter	142,800 km
Saturn	20,660 km
Uranus	51,400 km
Neptune	49,400 km
Pluto	2,280 km

The Sun's diameter is almost 10 times that of Jupiter, so it is too large to model to scale.

Diameters of the planets compared to Earth (approx)

Mercury	Venus	Earth	Mars	Jupiter	Saturn	Uranus	Neptune	Pluto
0.4	1	1	0.5	11	9.5	4.0	3.9	0.2

Uranus has a very faint ring. In fact Neptune and Jupiter also have almost invisible rings, but there is no point in modelling these.

Distances

The distances between the planets are vast. Some idea of the relative distances can be gained by measuring them to scale outdoors. A scale of 1 cm to represent 1 million km is suitable. It can then be seen that the planets near the Sun are relatively close together, while those farther away are a considerable distance apart. To this scale, Pluto, the planet furthest from the Sun, will be some 59 m from the person representing the Sun.

Approximate distance of the planets from the Sun in millions of km

Mercury	Venus	Earth	Mars	Jupiter	Saturn	Uranus	Neptune	Pluto
58	108	150	228	779	1427	2869	4497	5900

Painted scale pictures of the planets could be held up at each distance – as could scaled 3D models. But you won't be able to make the model of the Sun to scale, as it would be much too large.

Planet	Rotation period	Time to circle the Sun (Earth years)
Mercury	59 days	0.24
Venus	243 days 12 hours	0.62
Earth	23 hours 56 minutes	1.00
Mars	24 hours 37 minutes	1.88
Jupiter	9 hours 55 minutes	11.86
Saturn	10 hours 14 minutes	29.46
Uranus	10 hours 48 minutes	84.02
Neptune	15 hours 48 minutes	164.80
Pluto	5 days 9 hours	248.00

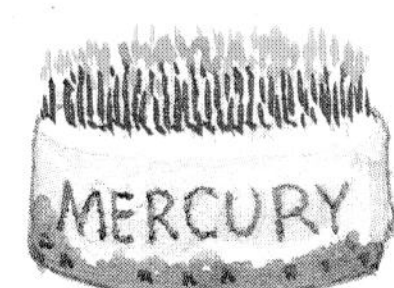

You would get lots of birthdays on Mercury but few in a lifetime on Saturn.

Making big numbers clearer

The sizes and distances expressed in dealing with objects in space are so large that we often express them in a mathematical notation. For example, 137,520 is written as 1.3752×10^5. Try this for the data on the planets in the table below.

The first example is done.

Planet	Distance from Sun (km)	Distance in mathematical notation	Diameter of planet (km)	Diameter in mathematical notation
Mercury	57,900,000	5.79×10^7	4,878	4.878×10^3
Venus	108,200,000		12,103	
Earth	149,600,000		12,756	
Mars	227,900,000		6,794	
Jupiter	778,900,000		142,800	
Saturn	1,427,000,000		120,660	
Uranus	2,869,000,000		51,400	
Neptune	4,496,700,000		49,400	
Pluto	5,900,000,000		2,280	

Library work

Astronomers over the centuries have found out a great deal about the planets. Some are solid, some are swirling masses of gas and liquid held down by gravity on to a rocky core. Some have moons of their own, some are so large that they exert a very big gravitational pull. The Voyager probes of recent time have suddenly added an immense amount to our knowledge of the planets. There is much for children to research in library books on the subject.

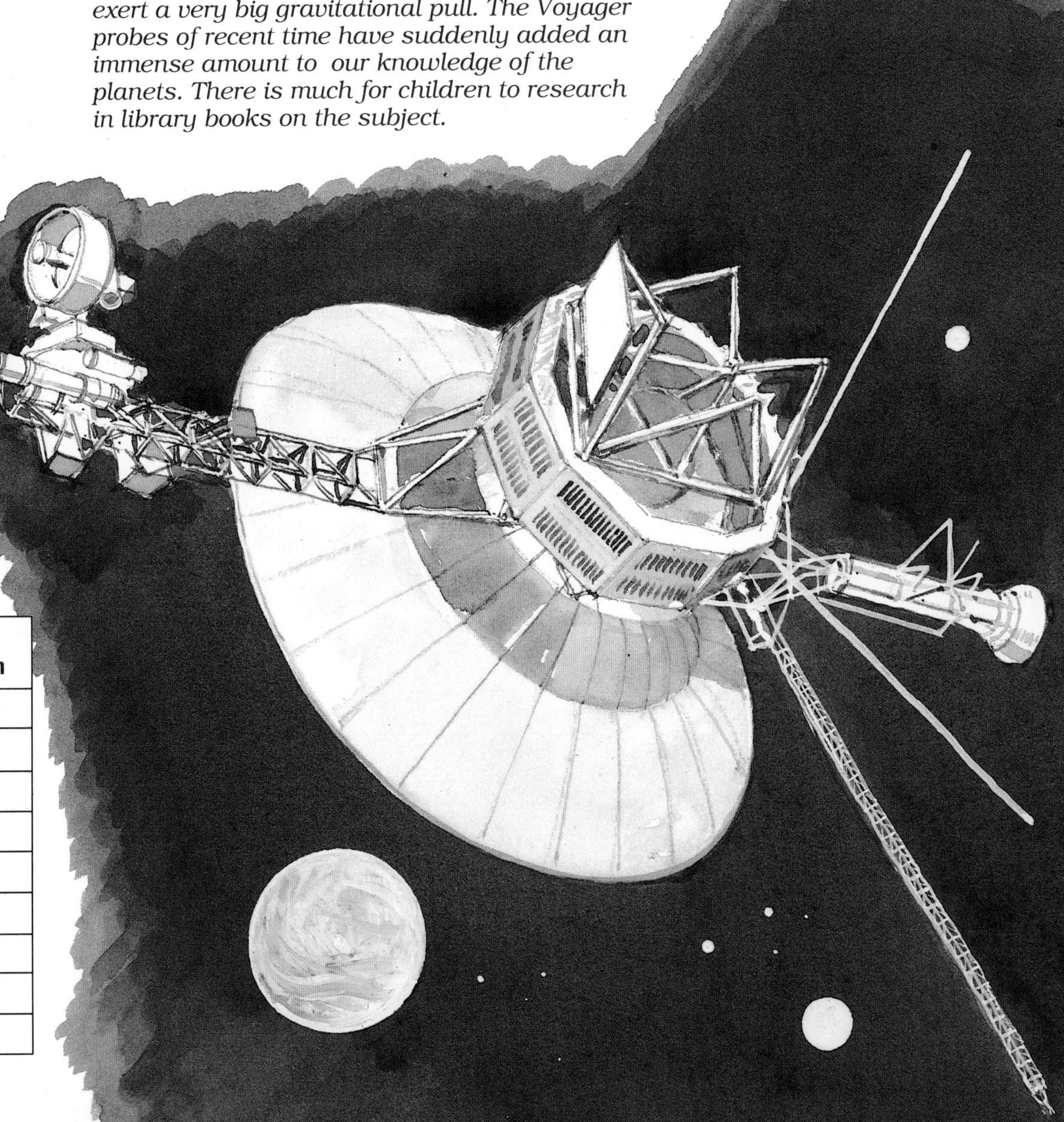

The stars are in reality suns. Each is an extremely hot mass of glowing gas. They appear faint because they are so far away. Some stars are bigger than others. Some stars are hotter than others. The hotter the star, the brighter it is. Many star names are derived from Arabic, since it was Arabic culture that continued the pursuit of scientific knowledge during the dark days of the Middle Ages in Europe when science was virtually forgotten.

Star rotation

Put a screw eye into the end of a 1.5 m rod. Stand the rod in a 3 litre plastic bottle filled with soil or sand which acts as a support.

Use a star map to identify a constellation and look through the screw eye in order to line up one of the stars in that constellation with the top of a lamp post, or a tree, or a rooftop.

Look for the star at 10 minute intervals. Does it appear to move?

Check other stars. Check the Pole Star!

The stars appear to revolve anticlockwise around the Pole Star. This is caused by the Earth spinning beneath the heavens. 'An Early Start to Nature', page 61, gives details for making a star clock based on this phenomenon. It also suggests some activities to carry out on constellations.

Using star maps

Star guides such as those produced by George Philip and Son Ltd are ideal for identifying constellations and individual stars. It is best to orientate yourself so that you face due south before you begin star spotting.

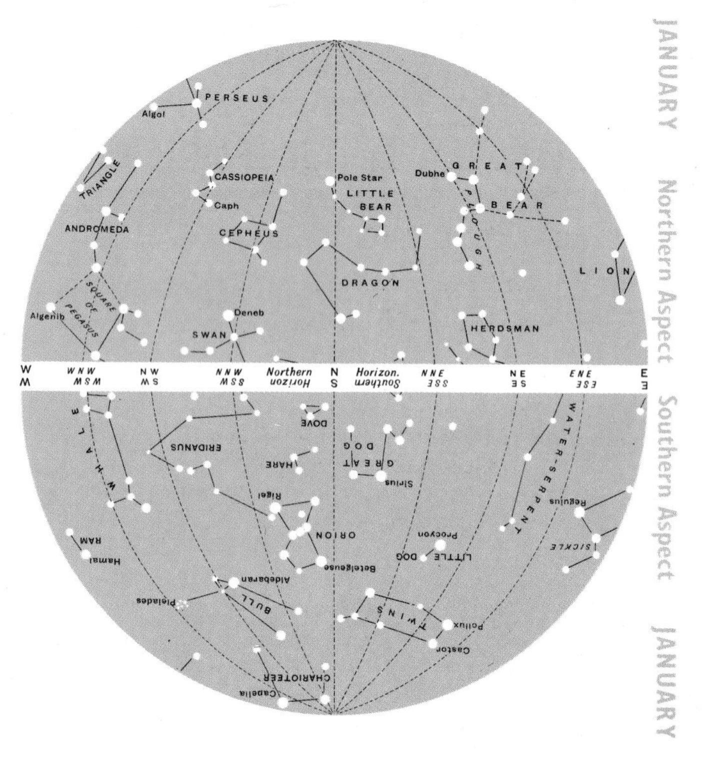

Brightness

Star brightness depends on how big the star is, how hot it is, and how far away it is.

How big?

Use the cardboard tube from a kitchen or toilet roll. Cover one end with black paper.

Prick holes of various sizes in the paper.

Put a lit torch into the tube and stand it on a table. Stand well away and advance toward the dots of light until you can just see each one.

Record the distance.

'Star Size'	Distance seen
Pin hole	
Compass needle hole	
Biropoint hole	
Knitting needle hole	

How hot?

This time use two torches of equal power, one shaded with tissue paper, the other left as normal. The black paper covering each tube should bear an equal sized hole.

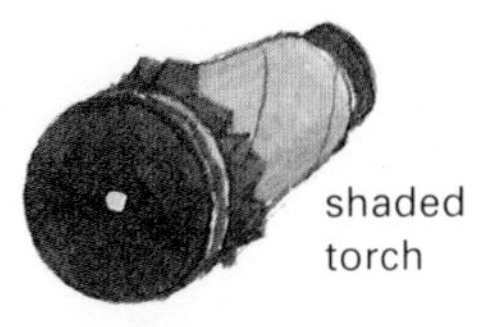

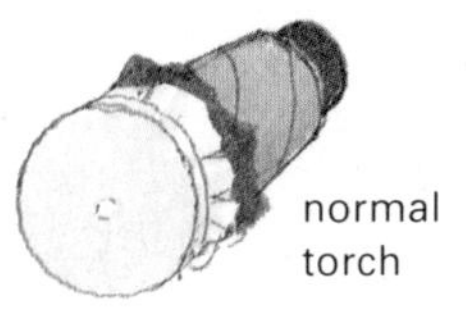

How far away?

Just move the tube, with one pinprick of light, farther and farther away from watching children.

Measuring brightness

Astronomers have a scale for measuring brightness.

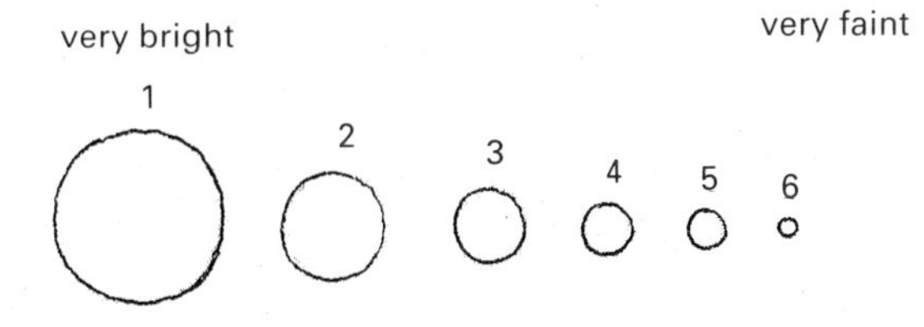

A star with a magnitude of 1 is very bright. Even brighter stars have magnitudes down to 0 and below – the brightest star, Sirius, has a magnitude of -1.58.

The faintest stars we can see with the naked eye have a magnitude of 6.

Each step on the scale is 2.5 times less bright than the one before. A magnitude 1 star is thus 100 times brighter than a magnitude 6 star. Telescopes will show up much fainter stars with magnitudes far beyond 6.

Try judging this scale against some easily spotted constellations. This is the scale for the stars of Orion, which dominates the winter sky.

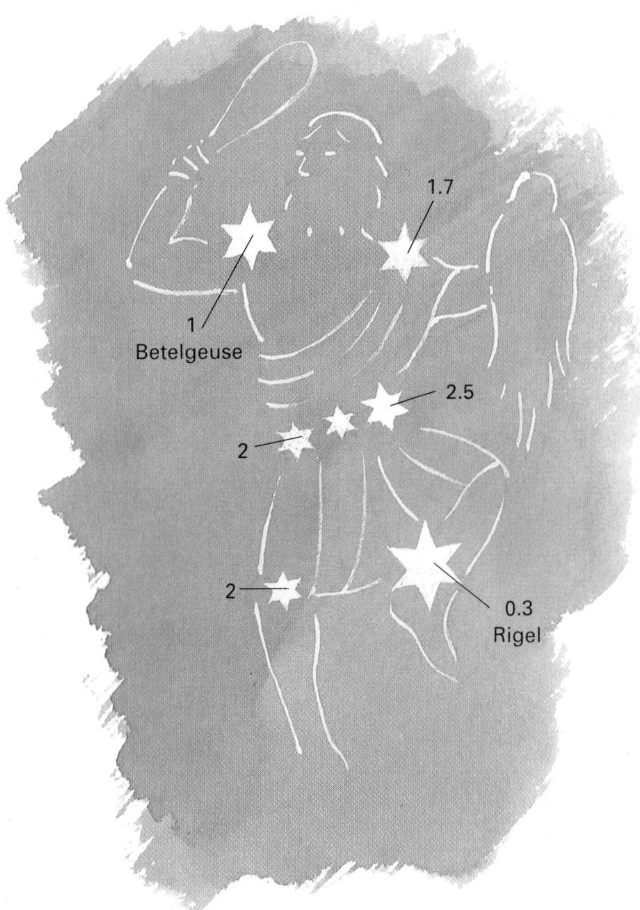

Betelgeuse is a reddish colour. Its temperature is 3000 K.

Rigel is bluish white and very hot. Its temperature is 15,000 K.

Trace the two templates shown below on to card to make a flying model of the Shuttle.

Cut them out. Score the dotted lines. Cut where shown.

Join the main wings to the fuselage by slotting them into place.

Strengthen with tape above and below.

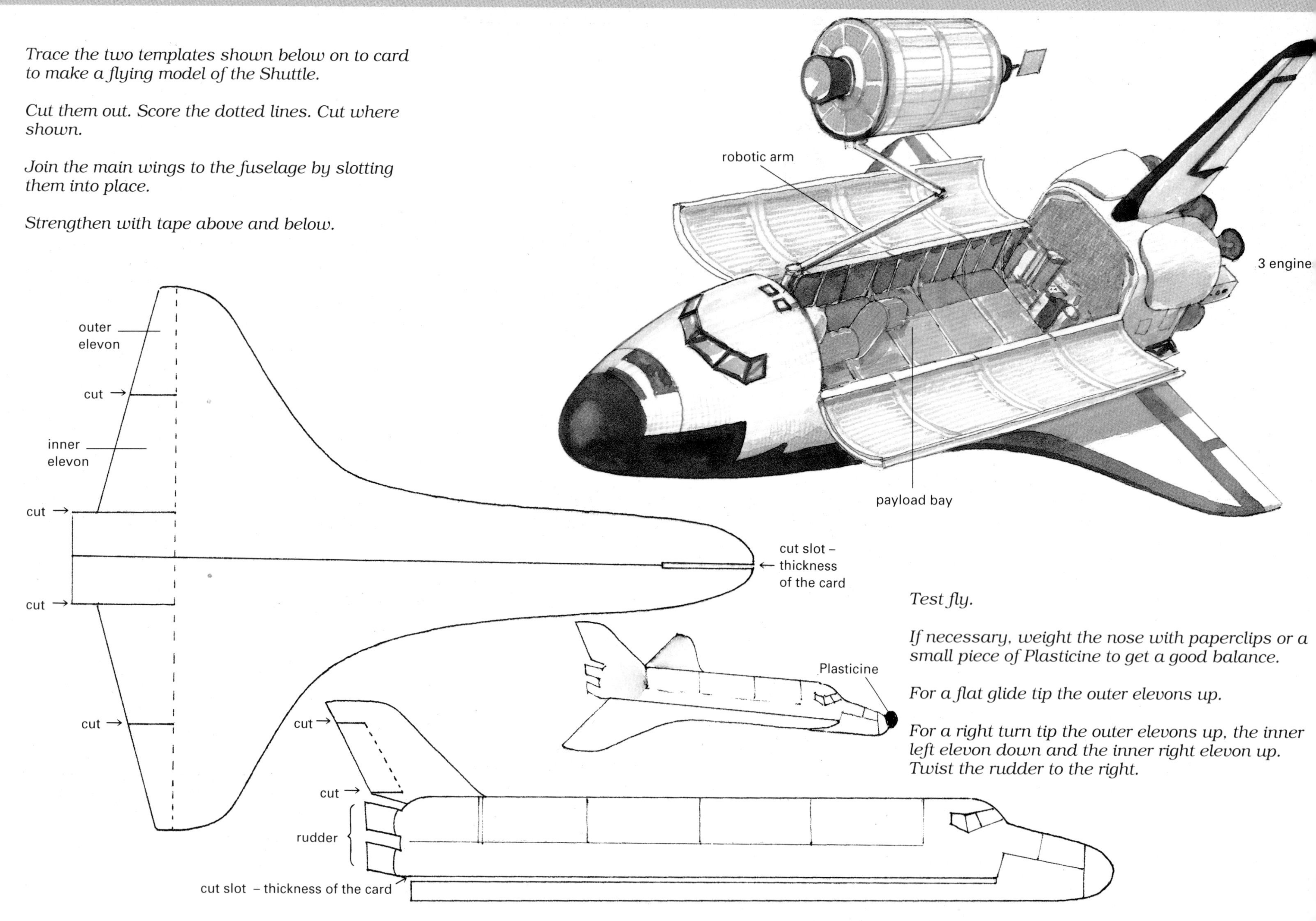

Test fly.

If necessary, weight the nose with paperclips or a small piece of Plasticine to get a good balance.

For a flat glide tip the outer elevons up.

For a right turn tip the outer elevons up, the inner left elevon down and the inner right elevon up. Twist the rudder to the right.

This is the Saturn V three stage rocket used to send the Apollo spacecraft to the Moon between 1969 and 1972.

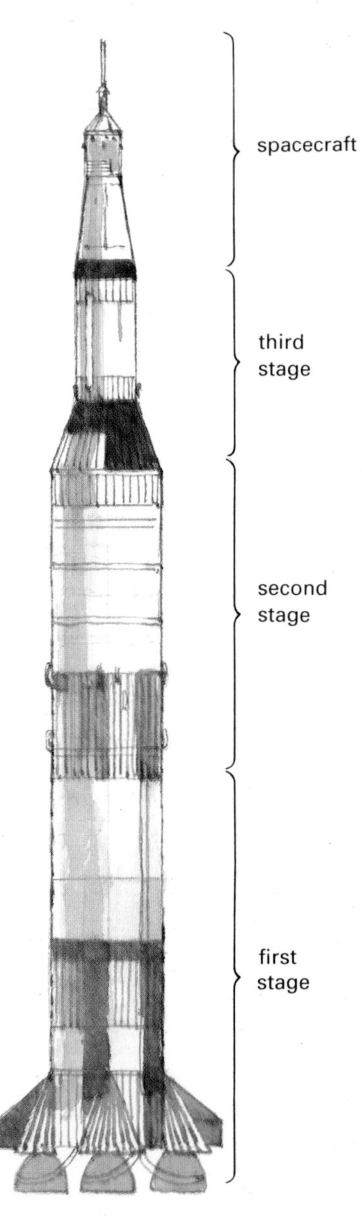

A model rocket

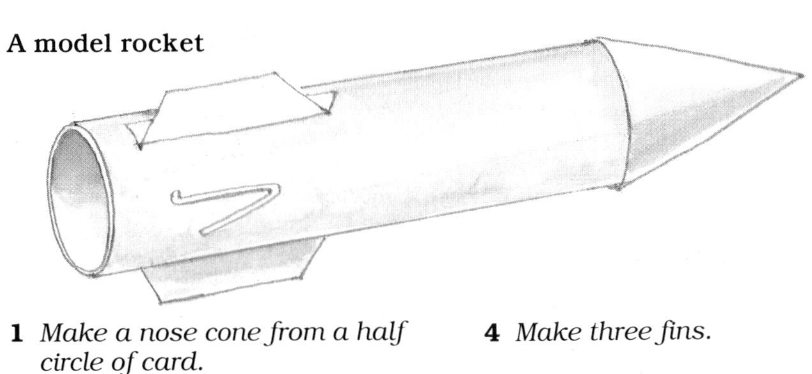

1 *Make a nose cone from a half circle of card.*

7 cm radius

2 *Push Plasticine as a nose weight into the cone.*

3 *Stick the nose cone to a kitchen paper towel roll body.*

4 *Make three fins.*

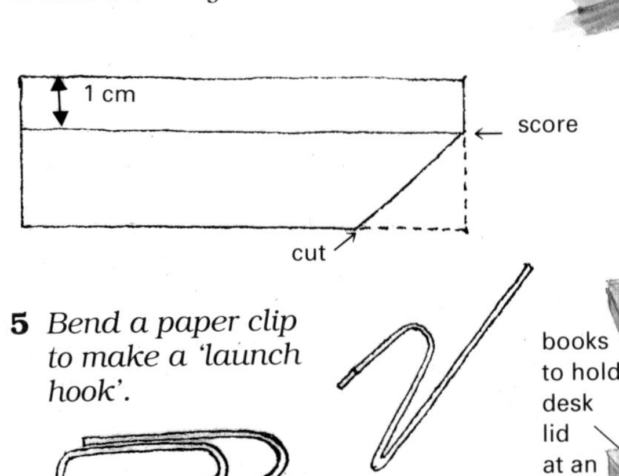

5 *Bend a paper clip to make a 'launch hook'.*

6 *Push the 'launch hook' into the body. Pinch it tight. Secure it inside and out with masking tape.*

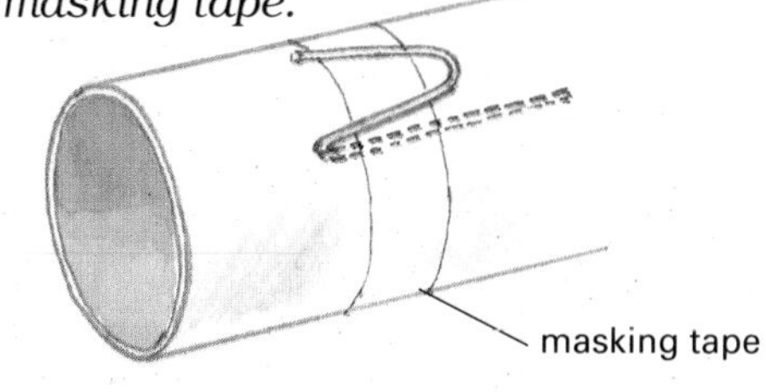

7 *Stick the three fins by their flaps to the body.*

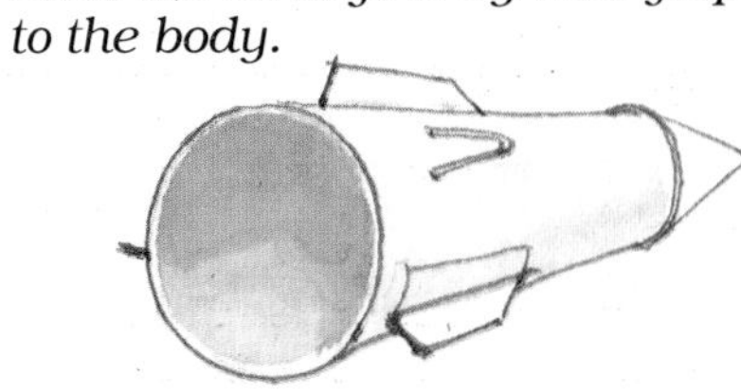

8 *Make a launch pad for the rocket.*

desk lid

books to hold desk lid at an angle

launch pad

9 *Record your results.*

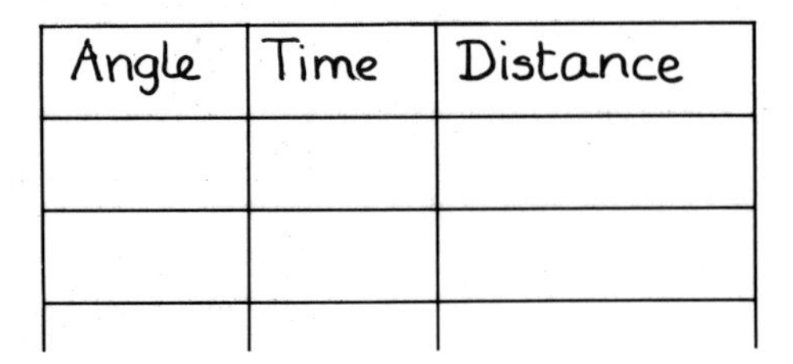

Angle	Time	Distance

NES Arnold Ltd
Ludlow Hill Road
West Bridgford
Nottingham
NG2 6HD
Telephone: 0602 452204

Griffin & George Ltd
Bishops Meadow Road
Loughborough
Leicestershire, LE11 ORG
Telephone: 0509 233344

Philip Harris Ltd
Lynn Lane
Shenstone
Staffordshire, WS14 OEE
Telephone: 0543 480077

Berol Ltd
Oldmedow Road
Kings Lynn
Norfolk, PE30 4JR
Telephone: 0553 761211

RS Components
PO Box 427, 13-17 Epworth Street
London, EC2P 2HA
Telephone: 071-253-1222

(continued)